1

Norwich, July 1981

Alison Hyslop ran down the stairs, taking them two at a time, almost knocking her father over as she rushed into the living room.

'I can't find my shoes!' she wailed. 'Oh, Mum, I can't find my shoes and they're the only decent pair . . . '

'Look in the kitchen, Alison,' her mother said, pulling a strand of knitting wool from the ball at her side.

John, Alison's father, winced as his daughter ran back upstairs to her room.

'She makes more noise now than when she was little,' he remarked. 'All this fuss for a party!'

'It isn't every day your boyfriend graduates with first-class honours, John! Let's face it, this graduation ball is something extra special.'

'And there she goes again.' John raised his eyes towards the ceiling and pulled a face. 'That same record, over and over.'

'It's her favourite, John Lennon. Be patient, she's in love.'

'Love?' He frowned. 'Do you really think it's that serious?'

'Of course it's that serious!' Anne teased him. Then, lowering her voice, she leaned forward and added, 'In fact, I've a feeling that there'll be an important announcement made tonight!'

'What kind of announcement?' John looked baffled. Then the truth slowly dawned on him. 'You don't mean . . . ?'

'Marriage, John! Now Adam's graduated, there's nothing to stand in their way. And Alison's teacher-training course has only a year to go. She'll make a good teacher, don't you think?'

'I think . . . ' John began, pointing his pipe at his wife ' . . . I think your daughter is calling you!'

When Anne got upstairs, Alison was standing in the middle of her bedroom,

TERESA ASHBY

A ONE-MAN WOMAN

Complete and Unabridged

LINFORD
Leicester

First published in Great Britain in 1990

First Linford Edition
published 2011

British Library CIP Data

Ashby, Teresa.
   A one-man woman. - -
   (Linford romance library)
   1. Widows- -Fiction. 2. First loves- -Fiction.
   3. Love stories. 4. Large type books.
   I. Title II. Series
   823.9'2–dc22

   ISBN 978–1–4448–0738–7

surveying herself in the full-length mirror.

'Oh, Alison, you look beautiful,' her mother declared, tears of pride welling in her eyes.

'Thanks for letting me have this dress, Mum.' Alison kissed her. 'I'll take good care of it. It's so beautiful.'

The dress was twenty years old and the soft, pinkish-red material contrasted sharply with the casual denim Alison usually wore.

She had altered it, of course, adding her own touches and accessories, to bring it up to date, but the style of the dress was timeless.

Anne blinked back her tears. Alison's cropped brown hair fitted the shape of her face perfectly and her deep-brown eyes made her appear innocent and much younger than her twenty years.

She had always been such a sensitive child, a true romantic, and Anne hoped fervently that nothing would ever happen to destroy that gentle part of her nature.

'Oh, you know, Mum,' Alison began, stars in her eyes, 'tonight's kind of special. I just know I'm going to remember it for ever.'

Just then, they heard Adam's car draw up outside and Alison ran down ahead of her mother. Adam came in, beaming all over his face and Alison's heart lurched with love for him.

He flicked back his fair hair, then she saw his brilliant blue eyes light up at the sight of her. She blushed. The effort had all been worthwhile, just for the pleasure in that look!

'Congratulations, son.' John shook his hand warmly. 'First class honours, eh? Well done! Have you time for a quick cuppa before you leave?'

'No, thanks, Mr Hyslop.' Adam looked at his watch. 'The car's been playing up and I want to allow us plenty of time to get to the ball.'

The Hyslops remained on the door-step, watching as the young couple walked down the path. Rarely had Anne seen two people who looked so right together. She turned and smiled at her husband and he nodded. He could see it, too!

After hurried goodbyes, Alison and Adam headed for the car. Adam opened the car door and made sure Alison was sitting comfortably before switching on the engine.

'I've something to tell you, later,' he said casually. 'But it'll wait.'

As they drove towards the university, Alison tried to keep her excitement in check and make casual conversation.

'Don't we have to pick up Tim tonight?'

'No!' Adam grinned. 'He's got himself a new girl and he's borrowed someone's car so he can make a good impression.'

Typical Tim! He always had a new girl. Not like her Adam! Adam was far more mature and settled. Alison let herself dream of the years ahead — years spent devoting her life to the man she loved.

'I'm glad he's fixed up,' she said out

loud, at the same time thinking, maybe that way he'll leave us alone for a change!

She was out of luck, though. When they arrived at the student union, Tim was waiting for them in the hall with his new girl clinging to his arm. She wasn't one of the usual crowd and seemed happy just to hang on to Tim and gaze adoringly at him.

He did have a kind of roguish charm, Alison realised, and she couldn't help liking him, despite the fact that so often he came between herself and Adam.

'Here he is now! The man of the moment, Mr Adam-Just-Call-Me-Genuis Simmons,' Tim shouted. 'With his lovely companion, Miss Alison Hyslop!'

Alison smiled tightly. If only Tim were a little more sensitive, then he would know that tonight was special and he'd keep out of their way!

'And this, friends, is Melanie,' he added, before depositing the unfortunate girl with Alison and leading Adam quite firmly towards the bar!

As the evening wore on, though, Adam pulled her on to his lap, nuzzling the back of her neck with his lips, reminding her that she was the special one.

'You've got a very kissable neck, you know, Alison Hyslop,' he murmured.

She closed her eyes, shivering with pleasure. Then he took her by the hand and led her quietly outside.

'There's something I have to say to you,' he said, as they passed through an ante-room. 'And it must be done in private.'

Oh, yes, Adam, yes, she thought happily.

Outside, she shivered in the cool night air and he draped his jacket around her shoulders. It was warm from his body and smelled deliciously of him. She looked up at him shyly, feeling faintly amused at his nervousness. He was obviously psyching himself up.

'Alison, I've been offered the chance of a research post, in America.'

'America?' Alison almost screeched. 'America?'

This wasn't what she'd expected him to say and, for a few moments, she was stunned, unable to grasp what he meant.

'California, actually. The job's like nothing I'll ever get here and I'll be allowed to work on my own designs.'

He was becoming more excited and, as he went on, Alison began to feel as though the ground was slowly crumbling beneath her feet. Anxieties and doubts began to needle their way through her happiness.

'It'll only be for six months,' he went on quickly, obviously before he lost his nerve. 'And, what I wanted to say was . . .'

He broke off, his eyes searching hers, a deep sadness in them as he tried to gauge her reactions. But, all she could do was stand, frozen on the spot. She had been so sure of him, so certain and now she didn't know what to expect.

'What I wanted to say,' he continued,

'is that I'm sorry it's worked out like this. But six months isn't so long! I know it sounds it now, but it isn't. It'll pass quickly. I've thought long and hard about being away from you and, believe me, it hasn't been an easy decision.'

'But, Adam, I thought,' Alison said, her voice hoarse with bottled-up tears, 'I thought that you and I . . . ' She couldn't say it, couldn't bring herself to lay bare her soul.

'Oh, Alison, you know that I think a lot of you and value your friendship, but we've our whole lives in front of us. Perhaps you thought I was ready for marriage, but I'm not. We're both far too young to make such a commitment!'

He reached out and touched her face gently.

'It's partly my fault I led you on, let you think . . . But I didn't mean to, Alison. Please believe me, I wouldn't have hurt you for the world. You mean far too much to me. And, when I come back . . . ' He fell silent, his unsaid

9

words containing a promise.

'I'd take you with me, of course, if I thought it would work,' he said gently. 'But it would be very wrong of me to ask you to give up your studies now. You've come too far, worked too hard. I couldn't watch you throw it all away, not for the sake of six short months.'

'But I don't care about my teaching, Adam. I just want to be with you!' she cried helplessly.

'You *will* be with me again, Alison, but you'll make a terrific teacher. You love kids and, believe me, you'd only resent me in years to come if you gave it all up now on my account.'

But how could she live without him, she thought. He *was* her life!

'Come on, you two!' The door flew open and Tim was shouting above the music. 'We want you in the photos.'

'With you in a minute,' Adam shouted to make himself heard. 'All right?' He turned back to Alison, tenderly taking her hand and encompassing it within her own. 'Are you ready to go back in?'

She nodded and, squeezing her hand tightly, Adam led her back into the hall and across the packed dance floor, the happy, laughing people dancing around.

Zombie-like, she lined up with her friends for a group photograph. She hardly noticed as the camera flashed, recording the moment for posterity . . .

★ ★ ★

Ten Years Later . . .

Alison smoothed her hand over a well-worn Aran sweater and, without warning, tears began to spill on to her cheeks.

It was over two months since she'd been widowed and it had taken her this long to find the courage to sort through her husband's things. Two months, hardly any time at all out of a lifetime!

What to do with it all posed no problem. Tim's parents had assured her, before they left for Australia, that they would like something from his personal effects.

She placed the sweater carefully in the box on top of the other things. Her mother had knitted for him and he rarely went boating without. It was just like a lucky mascot!

Last time, he'd left it at home — last time, he hadn't come back! She moved on quickly to a holdall she'd found in the bottom of his wardrobe and let out an involuntary gasp as she opened it.

Inside were many reminders of his school and university days. She unpacked it, placing things beside her on the bed. It was like a treasure chest ... his old school tie, his university scarf, the picture of them all at the graduation ball. She had no idea he'd kept all this. Tim had never been sentimental.

Then her fingers found a wad of tissue paper and, when she unwrapped it, she found the tiny silver cup that Tim and Adam had won as members of the rowing crew. How close those two had been back then and how she had envied the friendship they shared.

Oh, yes, she had always felt left out when they were together. Her fingers tightened around the cup as wave after wave of sorrow washed over her.

Thinking of those days so long ago — over ten years ago — made her realise that her youth had gone and, with it, all her chances of happiness. What hope was there now? It was too late . . . all too late.

She put the cup to one side. Perhaps Adam would like to have it, as a keepsake and reminder of his best friend. Tomorrow, Adam was coming to collect her, to spend the long school holidays with him and his wife, Barbara.

He'd been at the funeral, of course, but only briefly and there had been little time to talk. Besides, she had still been reeling from the shock of Tim's death.

Tim drowned! It was like a contradiction in terms. He was a remarkably strong swimmer, but this time his strength had not been enough to save him. She took a deep breath and rewrapped the cup. It would be good to see Adam again, chat about old times, find out what he'd been up to these past ten years.

Her spirits lifted slightly at the thought. Yes, it would be good to see him.

* * *

Adam Simmons hurried out of the print room. His tie was loosened, his shirt sleeves rolled up, and he carried a wad of fresh computer print-outs in his hand. It was evening and the building was virtually silent.

Adam walked into his office and closed the door firmly. There was a lot to be done if he were to take a whole day off to fetch Alison.

Just then, there was a light tap at the door and someone said. 'You still here, Mr Simmons?'

Adam looked up and smiled. Sam, the security guard, patrolled the building at night and would often, like now, just appear at the door. He was an ex-policeman with a sharp eye and an excellent reputation.

'I'm just about to leave, Sam,' Adam said. 'I've done enough today!'

Sam nodded. He often found Mr Simmons at his desk late at night and, occasionally, they would share a last cup of coffee and a friendly chat. That's what Sam liked about Mr Simmons. He treated everyone as equals.

'There's a gentleman downstairs to see you,' he told Adam now. 'He says he should have been here earlier, but his plane was delayed. He sounds American, Mr Simmons.'

'That'll be Gerry Peterson.' Adam smiled happily, some of his weariness evaporating. 'Ask him to come on up, would you, Sam? I'm expecting him.'

The security man hurried away and Adam began to clear his desk. Gerry Peterson was a valued friend. He owed him a great deal. Gerry had been there when Adam first arrived in the States, over ten years ago, no more than an inexperienced youth.

In those days, he'd had the cheek to think he knew it all. But Gerry had soon put him straight, offering him some valuable advice and making him think out his future far more clearly. Gerry worked for the American side of the company, selling computer software which Adam designed.

'Hey, Adam!' The door flew open and Gerry strode smartly in, a huge grin lighting up his tanned face. 'Working hard?'

'Just catching up really,' Adam explained. 'I'm taking the day off tomorrow and I wanted to get ahead.'

'So, what's the big occasion tomorrow? You celebrating something?'

Adam's expression grew grave then. 'Do you remember me telling you about Tim Johnstone? We were at school together and stayed best friends all through university, too.'

'Sure, I remember.'

'Well, tragically, he drowned in a boating accident, just over two months ago. I'm going to Norwich tomorrow to fetch his widow.'

'Gee, I'm sorry to hear that, Adam.' Gerry looked sympathetic. 'Were there any kids?'

Adam shook his head.

'Didn't you tell me that Tim married an old girlfriend of yours?' Gerry snapped his fingers as he remembered.

'That's right. He married Alison Hyslop. She's all alone now. Well, to be honest with you, Gerry, I'm worried about her. I've always felt a bit guilty about how I left her behind ten years ago when I first went to the States.'

Gerry nodded. Yes, he remembered Alison, the young girl who had written to Adam such a lot at first.

Then, as he recalled, Adam had to be pretty firm with her about breaking things off once and for all.

'Just as well she didn't wait for you,' Gerry remarked.

'Yes.' Adam smiled ruefully. 'That initial six months turned into ten years! But I couldn't have come home even if I'd wanted to, Gerry. Exciting things were happening in Silicon Valley and I wanted to be part of it all. As it turned out, I made the right decision.'

'You sure did,' Gerry agreed. 'I'd say things turned out pretty well for you.'

'And for Alison and Tim, too,' Adam said. 'I was pleased when those two got together.'

'You've done well in your private life, too,' Gerry pointed out. 'Barbara's a great girl, you know. Everyone adores her. She's been good for you, Adam.'

'Yes. I guess some would say I left it a bit late to get hitched, but now I'm an old married man of two years and no regrets.'

'Better late than never,' Gerry said, his smile faltering. 'Take it from one who knows. Once you've found a good girl, hang on to her! If I have any regrets at all about my life, it's not having found the right woman to share it with. It can get pretty lonely at times. Mark my words, Adam, you'll never make a sounder investment than that marvellous wife of yours!'

He looked concerned for a moment before adding, 'She understands about Alison?'

'She knows we were friends, yes,' Adam said evasively.

'I see.' Gerry nodded.

★　★　★

Alison had been watching out of the window all morning, waiting for the first glimpse of Adam's car.

Suddenly, an impressive silver car slid to a halt outside and she hurried to the door. How different this car was to the battered old jalopy he had driven in their student days!

She opened the door and watched as Adam walked confidently up the path towards her. He saw her waiting and grinned and something suddenly hit her. She wasn't prepared for this strange rush of feeling that engulfed her. That walk, those long, loping strides and that smile . . . the smile that said so much!

He had been good-looking as a young man but, now, the passing years had added strength to his features, chiselling out his fine good looks.

She had hardly noticed him at the funeral, but then, that was hardly surprising.

'Hi, Alison,' he said, but she just couldn't speak. She hadn't expected to feel like this, crushed by her own feelings.

Oh, she knew that seeing him again was likely to arouse all kinds of confusing feelings and memories, but this . . .

'You look a little peaky,' he went on, his blue eyes searching hers, concern showing in the dark blue depths. 'Are you taking care of yourself?'

She nodded, swallowing hard. 'It was good of you to come,' she said, her voice coming out clipped and precise, as if she'd been rehearsing that little speech all morning.

'Not at all. After all, that's what friends are for,' he said. 'Besides, Barbara and I are looking forward to having you stay with us. You'll be our first house-guest since we arrived in Britain.'

Alison stared at him. Barbara! How could she have forgotten that he was married now?

'Do you feel up to eating out?' Adam was saying. 'I thought we could grab a bite in Norwich, then drive down to Berkshire afterwards.'

She heard Adam's voice, but just couldn't think straight. He moved closer, seeing that she was in some distress and the sudden closeness of him, the delicate smell of his aftershave and the warmth of his hands touching her skin, were all too much to bear and she broke down and wept bitterly against his chest. His arms went about her instantly, holding her tight.

'Don't cry, Alison.' He soothed her,

stroking her hair gently. 'It's going to be all right, now. Don't worry.'

* * *

Barbara Simmons stood up wearily from her study desk, yawning.

This latest assignment was the most taxing of her career so far. It was only a small contract for a television company, working on the graphics for a new game show, but it required all her concentration and she just couldn't give it today.

She turned abruptly and moved quickly about the room, taking small, busy steps like a nervous cat as she checked and re-checked that everything was in its place, everywhere was tidy.

Adam would have laughed at her, but she wanted everything to be so right for this old friend of his. It was this very vulnerability, this lack of confidence in herself that had drawn Adam to her. He said she needed looking after! She stopped before a large mirror and glared at her reflection.

First, he said, he had noticed her beauty. She didn't think she was beautiful, but Adam had always insisted that it was her looks that had captivated him long before he even spoke to her. Her blonde hair wasn't too bad, she supposed, but her mouth was too large and her nose too small, she was sure.

She still saw herself as the plain, skinny kid with freckles and the statutory brace on her teeth. She certainly didn't see anything special when she looked at her reflection.

She paced around the room, moving her wedding photograph slightly to one side. What a wedding it had been! She still shuddered to think of it. Five hundred guests! She hated being the centre of attention.

They had met at a party given by a big record company. Adam had been working on some computer software for the firm and Barbara had been fulfilling her first major contract, designing the graphics for an exciting new pop video, which had quickly sped to the number-one position in the American charts.

The sound of distant, off-key singing interrupted her thoughts and made her smile. Jess was busy in the kitchen, getting things ready for the arrival of their guest. Thank goodness for Jess. Where would they be without her?

She had tried, bless her, to teach Barbara the rudiments of cooking, but as far as the culinary arts were concerned, Barbara didn't have a clue. It was ironic when she thought about it. She had attended the best schools in America, the finest finishing schools in Europe, and they had all given up on her where cookery was concerned.

So I can't cook, Barbara thought defiantly, but I'm a good graphic designer and I've landed some pretty lucrative new contracts lately! I'd rather be good at one thing than a Jill-of-all-trades.

Who are you trying to kid, Barbara Simmons, she thought grimly! The one thing, the one solitary thing she wanted most to give her husband, was the baby they both longed for.

They'd decided to start a family straightaway, as they wanted to have kids while they were still young enough to enjoy them. In the two years they'd been married, she'd been unable to conceive. No doctor could explain why.

'All right, love?'

She jumped and turned round quickly to see Jess, the housekeeper, standing in the doorway, looking concerned.

Jess was small, with untidy brown hair which had turned peppery around the edges, but she was a brilliant cook and kept the house spotless.

'Can you come through? I'll show you what's to be done.'

Barbara followed her to the kitchen and immediately was met by the most delicious smells.

'It won't spoil if dinner's a little late, so don't panic. I've made a green salad to go with the lasagne, so just give it a

25

bit of a turn and a splash of dressing before you serve it.

'The mousse is in the fridge. Before you serve that, whip up some cream and swirl it on the top, then scatter some chocolate vermicelli over it. OK?'

'Oh, Jess, it's wonderful. You've done us proud again.'

Jess smiled, her round face lighting up as she unbuttoned her overall.

'Will you be coming tomorrow?' Barbara asked hesitantly.

'Naturally,' Jess said with a grin. 'I'm too curious about your visitor to stay away.'

Her eyes took on a troubled look then as if she had remembered something and she added, 'I may have to bring Nicola with me, though.'

'Oh, do!' Barbara brightened. 'You know I don't mind.'

'Yes, but if you have company . . . '

'Oh, Mrs Johnstone is a school-teacher. She'll adore Nicola, too.'

Jess folded her overall and placed it carefully in her bag. Then with a final look around the kitchen, she headed for the door.

'The main thing is not to worry,' she called back. 'All you have to do is dish it up, then sit back and take all the credit!'

'Thanks, Jess.'

Barbara closed the door and made a mental note to add something extra to Jess's pay this week. Goodness knows, Jess could do with every penny.

She stood at the window and watched as Jess wheeled her bicycle on to the drive. There was a small seat on the back where Nicola liked to ride, which, at the moment, held a box full of groceries which Jess had to take to her next job.

Barbara shook her head in wonder. Jess was a marvel and seemed to have endless energy. As well as looking after her husband, two teenage children and little Nicola, she also did three house-keeping jobs, while Barbara could scarcely boil an egg without it ending in disaster!

She took a deep breath as Adam's car turned into the drive. The waiting was over!

Adam jumped out of the car and hurried round to open the door for Alison. She got out slowly and looked up at the imposing house, eyes widening in awe. Then she turned and said something to Adam which made him laugh.

Barbara should have gone out to greet them, she knew. Instead, she was staring at Alison Johnstone. She was not what she had expected at all. Alison was very pretty in an understated way.

Her lovely hair was swept back from her small, elfin face and her brown eyes seemed huge behind long, thick lashes. Adam was holding her arm protectively leading her towards the front porch.

Barbara pulled herself up mentally. Alison was a widow, for pity's sake! The poor woman must be feeling wretched. She hurried through to the hall to greet them.

'Hello, Alison. It's so nice to meet

you at last,' Barbara said warmly, extending her hand in a friendly greeting. 'Adam's told me so much about you.'

'Yes, we go back a long way together,' Alison said wistfully. She hadn't expected Barbara to be so stunning, or so softly spoken.

'So I've heard.' Barbara smiled and turned to Adam. 'Did you have a good drive, honey?'

'Not too bad.' Adam smiled warmly.

'We had some good times,' Alison was saying thoughtfully and Barbara felt a pang of sympathy.

She knew how shocked Adam had been to hear of his friend's death. How much greater must his widow's pain be!

Adam had been so looking forward to seeing Tim again when they returned from the States. He'd had such plans. She was glad now that she had suggested to Adam that they should have Alison to stay at Starlings Corner.

'I expect Alison would like to freshen up before dinner,' Adam suggested.

'Of course,' Barbara replied. 'I'll show you to your room.'

'What a lovely house,' Alison remarked as they went upstairs.

'Why, thank you!' Barbara smiled. 'It has so much character. Adam and I love it. Look, I've put you in here.' She opened the door into a large room. 'I hope you'll like it. The bathroom's through there. I'll leave you to it, then, and see how dinner is doing.' —

The windows were open and white net curtains billowed into the room, flattening out when Barbara closed the door as she left. The room was decorated in subtle hues of pink and grey, which had a very relaxing and calming effect on Alison. Obviously, Barbara had a magical touch when it came to decorating.

She sat down on the bed and touched the heavy, satin bedspread, thinking back over the day which had begun so strangely.

How easily the years had fallen away when she and Adam were together.

How strange it was that they still had so much in common. He could still make her laugh and she could still tease him.

'Why Berkshire, Adam?' she asked as they sat in the restaurant.

'Convenience,' he had replied. 'It's spot on for Heathrow, London and all the major routes within this country and Europe. I'm going to build a large complex in the country eventually, then I'm going to expand into Europe. It'll create hundreds of jobs, thousands even and . . .'

He had looked taken aback to see that she was laughing at him. 'Still the same old Adam,' she said. 'You've always known exactly where you were going.'

Her late husband, Tim, had always been overshadowed, somehow, by his best friend. She had to admit now that she'd married him on the rebound from Adam, and it was only when she had seen Adam walking up the path towards her that morning that she had realised what had been missing all these years

— the very special magnetism that was all Adam's own.

Oh, she'd loved Tim in a quiet sort of way and had worked harder at making a go of their marriage than she had ever worked for anything, but it was never a grand passion.

Tim was no fool. He'd realised early on that their marriage had been a mistake but, like Alison, he had tried to make it work. Yet it had all ended in indifference. There had been a time — a very brief period — when happiness had seemed possible for them.

Tim had been overjoyed when she'd told him she was pregnant and had thrown himself whole-heartedly into the whole business of impending fatherhood. It had drawn them closer than she'd ever have dreamed possible.

Then, tragedy had struck!

Two months before the baby was due, Alison had had an accident at school. She had been running down the stairs and had slipped, losing her footing and tumbling down.

When she'd awoken in hospital, it was all over. Tim was at her side, his face a white mask of anguish. Their baby, a little girl, had been stillborn.

Tim had been great at first, comforting her, looking after her, nursing her back to health, but this understanding had soon turned to resentment as her grief had lingered on over the months. She'd felt as if she had lost a part of herself and Tim could not understand.

After that, they'd both given up trying. There had been nothing left . . .

The grandfather clock in the hall chimed the quarter-hour and Alison suddenly remembered where she was. Adam and Barbara would be waiting and wondering.

Quickly, she went downstairs. It was important that Adam should not find out that so much of her marriage had been a failure. She owed Tim that much.

Several doors opened off the hall and she stopped for a moment, listening, until she heard Adam's deep voice and Barbara's soft response.

She moved towards an open door and, before entering, she saw Barbara standing with her back to the door, fixing Adam a drink. Adam had crept up behind his wife, slipping his hands around her waist and was nuzzling the back of her neck, making her twist and squirm and laugh softly.

'Adam!' Barbara whispered, embarrassed. 'Not now.'

'Can I help it if you've got the most kissable neck, Mrs Simmons?' Adam murmured.

Alison stepped backwards, totally unprepared for the utter rage that welled within her. How many times had he kissed her like that? How many times had he nuzzled the back of her neck?

In one, stark moment, a terrible truth dawned on her. None of her feelings for Adam had lessened over the years. Her thoughts were in a turmoil. Adam is married, she told herself. You've no right to feel like this.

But she couldn't help the way she felt. Adam's marriage was wrong! Barbara was not right for him! Confused, dizzy, she took a moment to try to compose herself.

Taking a deep breath, she propelled herself towards the door, ignoring the little voice at the back of her mind which told her to leave now, before it was too late, and walked confidently into the room.

Adam was hers. She loved him and this time she would fight to have him.

She would not lose him a second time!

2

'Time for a break!' Barbara had to raise her voice to make herself heard over the roar of the vacuum cleaner as Jess, the housekeeper, vacuumed the lounge carpet.

'Coffee!' she said in her soft, American accent. 'Come on, Jess, you've been hard at it since you arrived. You make me feel so lazy!'

Jess laughed as she switched off the vacuum and sat down.

'I don't know how you manage to do all you do. And talking of things to do, I saw Bob Jenkins in the village yesterday and he asked me to pass on a message about the wildlife sanctuary.

'He's arranging another meeting at the village hall and he wants you to handle the publicity. I told him you were busy and had a house guest, but he said you wouldn't mind.'

'I don't mind, really. I don't look on it as work, Jess, and it makes a nice change for me.' Barbara smiled.

Jess looked around curiously. 'Where's Alison this morning? She's usually pottering about in the kitchen.'

'Oh, you'd noticed,' Barbara said, and Jess thought that she sounded slightly annoyed. 'She's driven into town to buy some food. It's my father-in-law's birthday soon and we're having him over for a celebration meal. Alison insists on cooking it, of course, and she's determined to bake a cake.'

'That's kind of her,' Jess said. 'How is she now? She's only been here just over a week, but the improvement in her seems wonderful.'

'Yes, she seems to be coping very well,' Barbara said evasively.

The older woman sipped her coffee, feeling a wave of sympathy for Barbara. She was such a nice girl who was trying so hard to fit in. Yet, she hadn't an ounce of self-confidence and, since her arrival, Alison Johnstone had apparently sapped what little self-esteem Barbara might have had.

It wasn't anything Jess could put her finger on. Alison was never cruel or malicious, but Jess had the distinct feeling that she was always trying to get one up on Barbara.

'But?' Jess said then, and Barbara turned to look squarely at her.

'Oh, there's no hiding anything from you, is there, Jess? Alison's nice, but she's so . . . I don't know, capable, I suppose. She makes me feel so useless and I can't help wondering how that makes Adam feel about me.'

'He loves you, though,' Jess scolded gently. 'Mind you, it's only natural to be feeling insecure with your husband's ex-girlfriend staying in the house. Who wouldn't be? I know I would.'

'It sounds selfish, Jess, but Adam and I have so little time on our own as it is. Now we're having to entertain Alison all the time. Still, we're going to the theatre and a party in a couple of days with some clients of mine. Alison's coming, but Gerry's going to be there, too.'

'There's nothing for you to worry about, Barbara,' Jess said kindly, but even to her own ears she didn't sound very convinced.

Barbara lifted her shoulders as if she were trying to make a conscious physical effort to shrug off her worries.

'Let's not waste any more time talking about me. How are things at home? You've been working like a slave, it seems to me, and you looked so down-hearted when you came in this morning. Is something troubling you? Is the work too much?'

'Oh, no, of course not!' Jess said quickly, a note of panic in her voice.

The last thing she wanted or needed right now was to lose this job. She needed every penny she could get!

'Then what? Oh, come on, Jess. I've told you all my troubles, now it's your turn.'

'It's a lot of things.' Jess admitted. 'Pete's having an awful time just now.

39

He keeps applying for jobs only to be told he's too old. He's only forty-five but, as far as any future employers are concerned, he's over the hill.

'He's an active man, Barbara, and it's getting him down being stuck at home all the time. He feels he's letting us down. And then there's Nicola.'

'Is she no better?' Barbara frowned anxiously.

'No. I've been backwards and forwards to the doctor with her and he's finally agreed that there could be something more seriously wrong than he previously thought. He's going to arrange for her to see a specialist, but he said we'd be ages on the waiting list.'

'Oh, really!' Barbara said angrily. 'How long is this waiting list?

'He wouldn't say, but I gather it could run into months.'

'That's ridiculous!' Barbara exclaimed. 'There must be something I can do to help. I'll arrange for Nicola to see my doctor for a second opinion and he can refer her to a private specialist.'

'You'll do no such thing!' Jess threw up her hands in horror. 'I couldn't possibly afford it.'

'But I can, Jess.' Barbara smiled. 'Let me, please? It can be an early birthday present for Nicola. Say yes, Jess, for Nicola's sake.'

'I'll make it up to you,' Jess declared stubbornly, looking at Barbara through tear-filled eyes.

'I don't want that,' Barbara protested. 'I love Nicola. I just want to help her. I'd love children of my own,' Barbara said, eyes shining brightly. 'So would Adam. And, if I'm right, he won't have long to wait!'

Jess's expression brightened as realisation began to dawn. 'I thought as much!' she said, grinning all over her face as the tears vanished. 'So when is the baby due?'

'Oh, Jess.' Barbara blushed, but she was too full of happiness to keep the news to herself any longer. 'It hasn't been confirmed yet so I'm not certain.'

'But you're as sure as you can be?' Jess remarked.

'The signs are all there.' Barbara tried to keep her voice steady. 'Not a word to anyone though, Jess. I haven't even told Adam yet. You see, we've thought I was pregnant before and I'd hate to disappoint him all over again.'

Jess got up, walked around the table and put her hand on Barbara's shoulders. Just a moment ago, the pretty American had looked so happy and now she was looking utterly devastated.

'You'll have that baby one day, love. I know you will.'

Outside, in the hall, Alison had just come in from the shops and was heading towards the kitchen with two bulging carrier bags. The sound of Jess's voice halted her in her tracks.

She'd said something about a baby! Alison paused outside the half-open door for a moment and, almost without realising it, she began to listen.

'I don't know, Jess,' Barbara was

saying miserably. 'Adam longs for a child. We both do. We decided as soon as we married that we didn't want to wait. But, look at us. Two years gone by and nothing.'

'Don't dwell on it, Barbara,' Jess said. 'You can try too hard, you know. Besides, Adam didn't marry you to have children. He married you because he loves you.'

'But how long will he wait? I'm letting him down.'

Alison moved away from the door and slipped upstairs to her room to change. She couldn't go merrily into the kitchen now after what she'd just heard, nor was she quite sure how she felt about it.

Sorry for Barbara and Adam, of course, very sorry, but . . .

She pressed her hands against her stomach and it knotted. She could have children. The doctors had told her that there was no reason at all why she shouldn't have more babies.

'No!' she cried aloud, shocked when

she became aware of where her treacherous thoughts were leading. 'No!'

But the thought was there, however much she tried to deny it, rushing through her brain like a steam-roller, crushing any feelings she might have had of right or wrong. She could have a baby. She could so easily give Adam what Barbara could not.

* * *

The light-hearted play was good, but Barbara found herself unable to concentrate on it at all. There was so much on her mind.

Sitting at her side, Gerry was clearly enjoying himself immensely. Along the row, a million miles away from her, it seemed, Adam was sitting with Alison who, somehow, had managed to monopolise his company all evening.

She glanced at the man sitting behind them. Charles Mariner returned her unsteady smile. He was a good client

44

and he had put her name forward for a new contract which was to be the biggest thing ever to happen to her.

She looked again at Adam. He was whispering something to Alison and she was giggling. Their heads were so close that they almost touched. Barbara shuddered. Thank goodness the play was almost over. She wanted to be alone with Adam. No, more than that, she needed to be close to him again.

At last, though, the play was over. Barbara clapped her hands harder than anyone else, relieved that, maybe now, she could enjoy her own husband's company for a while, even if it was just at a party. Adam would be there beside her in a supportive rôle and she was determined Alison wouldn't gain the upper hand again.

They moved out into the foyer and, as they gathered together, she noticed that Alison kept touching her head with her fingertips.

'Is something wrong?' she asked, snapping more than she'd meant to.

'Nothing to worry about.' Alison smiled weakly. 'It's just a headache. It's been getting worse all evening.'

'What's up?' Adam asked, his face looking concerned. 'Not feeling well, Ali?'

Barbara felt stung. It was the first time she had heard Adam use a shortened version of Alison's name. Did that indicate some deepening in their relationship?

You're being silly, she told herself. Alison and Adam are old friends. They're bound to be close.

'A headache, Adam.' Alison smiled apologetically. 'Look, I don't want to be a nuisance, but I can't face the party right now. I'm sorry, Barbara, but I'd rather get back to Starlings Corner and have an early night. Perhaps you could get me a taxi, Adam?'

Barbara looked long and hard at Alison. Oh, how insensitive she'd been. Poor Alison. Occasions like these, when she and Adam and the Mariners were couples, must be hard on her, making her acutely aware of how alone she was.

No wonder she had a headache. She was so recently widowed. Of course she wouldn't want to go to a party.

'I'm not going to get you a taxi,' Adam said. 'I'll drive you home myself.'

'Oh, please, don't go to any trouble,' Alison protested lamely. 'I don't want to spoil the evening for everyone else.'

'It's all right, Alison,' Barbara argued. 'We'd all feel much happier if Adam ran you home.' She turned to her husband. 'You go on, darling. I'll be all right.'

'I feel such a nuisance,' Alison remarked.

'I'm just sorry the evening has been ruined for you,' Barbara said sympathetically.

They made their apologies to the Mariners and Barbara watched them leave, a lump forming in her throat. She felt very alone now, despite the fact that she was among friends.

She watched as Adam put his hand on Alison's waist and led her through the doors, and couldn't help shivering.

'We'll get a cab to take us on to the party,' Charles Mariner announced. 'Do you think Adam will join us later?'

'I don't know,' Barbara said, her voice small. 'I doubt it.'

Alison sat quietly in the passenger seat of Adam's car and closed her eyes as he steered them out of the town and on to the pitch-black country roads.

It hit her suddenly that, for the first time since she'd arrived, they were alone together. With this thought, the headache she had genuinely been suffering from, seemed to lessen a little.

Alison's heart began to race as they neared the house. Alone at last with Adam! Stop it, she told herself, but she had had one drink too many and that was enough to suffocate any inhibitions she may have had.

When the car stopped outside the house, Adam turned to face her.

'All right?' he asked softly.

He sounds different, she thought wildly . . . as if . . . She nodded and got out of the car, stumbling on the gravel path and wrenching her ankle.

'Hang on.' Adam was by her side at once and his arm went around her waist to support her. Gratefully, she leaned against him. 'Dizzy?' he said.

'A little,' she lied.

Thank goodness it was dark so he wouldn't see her cheeks redden guiltily. But he was holding her tight and his touch was only adding to the confusion already in her mind.

'I think you should go straight to bed,' Adam suggested gently, leading her carefully towards the stairs.

She hoped this would last as long as possible for, all the time they were climbing the stairs, Adam had his arm tightly around her.

When he opened her bedroom door, she said, 'Don't turn on the main light, Adam. The table lamp will be softer.'

Adam nodded. Of course, the bright, overhead light would make her head feel worse. He held on to her as he located the bedside lamp and, when he clicked it on, Alison gasped. He looked wonderful, with his hair ruffled and his tie loose against his shirt, which was open at the neck.

He lowered her gently on to the bed and kneeled down so that he could ease her shoes off her feet. As his fingers brushed against her leg, she shivered with delight.

'Can you manage to get youself ready for bed, Alison?' he asked, looking at her with his intense blue eyes.

'I think so,' she stammered, her voice a ragged whisper.

His face was so close to hers that she could feel the warmth of his breath on her cheek. She closed her eyes, waiting, but he stood up.

'I'll get you some aspirins and a glass of water while you get ready for bed,' he said, turning and walking from the room.

As soon as he had gone, she stood before the mirror and watched herself undress. It was like looking at a stranger. Could this alluring, desirable woman really be her? She smiled as she got into bed. The sheets felt deliciously cool against the warmth of her skin and she sat up, holding the covers coyly around her, as she waited for his return.

Her heart was hammering and she knew full well that, without the two or three drinks she'd had earlier, she would never have had the nerve to behave like this.

But she was doing nothing wrong, she reasoned. She loved Adam, always had and, once he realised that they were meant for each other, everything would be all right.

Adam came back, carrying a glass of water, but his eyes widened in surprise when he saw her sitting up in bed.

He walked towards her, trying to keep his gaze averted. The last thing he wanted to do was embarrass her, but she was obviously feeling quite unwell and was unaware of what she was doing.

'Sit down, Adam,' she murmured, and he sat beside her on the bed and handed her the glass and tablets.

'Thank you, Adam,' she whispered, 'for everything.'

'That's all right, love,' he said hoarsely.

She took the aspirins and swallowed them, aware all the time that only the thin sheets existed between them.

She was remembering a time, years ago, when he would have been only too eager to take her in his arms. But he was older now, more restrained.

'Adam,' she began, 'oh, Adam . . . '

She leaned forward and he put his arms around her. She could feel his heart thumping fast through his shirt, smell the spicy tang of his after-shave, feel the warmth of his body. She felt so small, warm and safe locked in his arms.

Adam didn't know what to do for the best. Alison was clearly heartbroken and still deeply affected by Tim's death. He was all too aware of her vulnerability yet, at the same time, he couldn't fail to realise that she was a very attractive woman, not just an old friend, not just Tim's widow.

If only Barbara had come home with them, she would have known exactly what to do.

'There now,' he said soothingly. 'Settle down.'

He pushed her back against the pillows and pulled the covers up around her.

'Those pills should do the trick fairly soon and then you must try to get some sleep. It's very late and you need to rest.

'Now, if you're comfortable,' he began, 'I'll go on to the party. That's if you're sure you'll be all right here on your own. I can always make you a cup of tea, or cocoa, or something?'

No, her mind screamed. Stay, stay with me! But she could only say, 'No, no, you go on to the party.' Her voice was a timid whisper, tinged with shame.

He moved towards the door, pausing to look back at her for a few moments before disappearing out on to the landing.

What had happened? She had thought

she had him right in the palm of her hand, so what had gone wrong?

Tears welled in her eyes and, as she heard the front door slam, they spilled out on to her cheeks. She had been so close, so close, and she had let the moment slip by. How could she have been so stupid?

Turning her face into her pillow, she muffled her heartbroken sobs and tried not to listen as the car engine purred away into the night.

* * *

'Are you glad we chose you to do this work, Barbara?' Charles Mariner said soberly, and, for a moment, Barbara's smile faded as the uproar of the party continued.

'Oh yes, yes I am,' she said eagerly.

'Good. You know there were two of you on the short list and you won. I saw to it personally. The other person had more experience, but I felt sure that you, with your flair, were the right one for the job.'

There was a question in his steady gaze and Barbara felt confident as she gave him her answer.

'I won't let you down, Charles,' she said positively.

'I know.' He grinned.

Charles Mariner excused himself and went over to the buffet table.

Doubts began to assail Barbara now she was sitting alone. Was she taking on too much? Suppose Adam didn't understand? He had always been supportive so far, but the nature of both their careers meant that they saw relatively little of each other.

And now there was the baby to consider — perhaps, she reminded herself, it was only perhaps. But things didn't seem quite right between her and Adam just now, and she didn't want her work to become a wedge between them.

What if he really was fed-up with her, her inability to have children, to cook, to do all the things a wife should do for the man she loves?

Adam isn't like that, she told herself, at least he wasn't, until Alison turned up to demonstrate her skills!

'Jean, Jean, door!' someone yelled to the hostess.

The music stopped and there was a brief lull in the noise with only the hum of conversation to take its place.

She felt so alone, wondering what Adam was doing right now. Was he sitting with Alison? He should be here, sharing her success, but Alison needed him and Barbara felt ashamed for thinking badly of her.

Suddenly, as another record, a slow one this time, was played, she saw him standing in the doorway, his eyes never leaving hers until he was right at her side.

★ ★ ★

Barbara smiled politely at her mother-in-law and looked at Alison. Ever since the night of the party, her house-guest had been behaving most oddly. Maybe

56

the headache was the kind that lingered for days. Barbara couldn't think what else could be wrong with her.

Yet, since Adam's parents had arrived, Alison had perked up no end. She wished Gerry was still here, if only to make up the numbers. He had gone to the West Country for a while and, without him, Barbara felt very much on her own, somehow, especially now.

'That was delicious,' David Simmons said, folding his napkin carefully and placing it beside his empty plate.

'Alison's a wonderful cook,' Barbara said at once. 'She did all the cooking tonight. I just did the washing up!'

Alison smiled modestly and, once again, Barbara felt that pang of uselessness that Alison so easily stirred inside her.

Even when Adam had told his parents about Barbara's marvellous new project, they had seemed quite unimpressed and had gone on to praise Alison's cheese sauce!

'It was Alison's idea to make you a

cake, Dad,' Adam said, smiling appreciatively at their guest.

'You always were a good cook, Alison,' Jennifer Simmons remarked.

Barbara sighed and forced a smile. Ever since they'd arrived, the Simmonses had been full of the 'good old days' when Adam and Alison were together!

It had become crystal clear, too, that they had been more than just good friends. From what the Simmonses had said, the two of them were virtually standing at the altar when Adam had left for the States.

She'd had enough of their happy reminiscences and jokes and she could feel herself being pushed, not deliberately, of course, but pushed, nevertheless, to the outskirts. And once again, Alison had managed to sit beside Adam, and the more Barbara looked at the two of them, the more she realised how right they looked together.

Once that thought had struck her, she couldn't stop dwelling on it. The more she tried not to look at them, the more it ate away at her. Everything each said or did was in tune with the other.

They were like the married couple and Barbara the guest! And Adam's parents, whether intentionally or not, were treating Alison as their hostess and daughter-in-law. The wedge was there all right and everyone seemed to be driving it deeper, widening the gulf which had once been no more than a tiny crack.

'Excuse me,' Barbara said suddenly.

She pushed back her chair. She had to get away, get out of the room and gather her thoughts and try to make some sense of her turbulent feelings.

'I'll make some coffee,' she announced nervously. Surely she couldn't mess that up!

She left the dining room, shutting the door behind her and leaning against it. Dr Macey had told her to call tomorrow, but perhaps if she gave him a ring now, he would know. She glanced at the door, satisfying herself that the occupants were too engrossed to bother with her and hurried over to the telephone.

If only she could tell Adam the news tonight! Then he could tell his parents and, for once, she would have done something right. She sat down on the stairs so that she was half-hidden behind the banister and picked up the telephone. Her hands shook as she dialled the number and it seemed to take for ever before the doctor's wife came to the phone.

'Hello, Sarah. It's Barbara Simmons. Could I have a word with Jeff, please?'

'Of course, Barbara. I'll just get him.'

She waited for what seemed an eternity, then heard the sound of someone picking up the phone.

'Barbara? Hello. You're ringing for the results, aren't you?'

'Yes.' She held her breath. He knew how eager she was, how desperate.

'I'm sorry, Barbara,' he began and she knew right away, without his actually saying it, what the result had been. 'I'm afraid the test was negative. You're not pregnant. Are you still there, Barbara?'

'Yes,' she said shakily.

She felt as if she had been punched in the stomach, knocked to the ground. Her head spun, her eyes seemed heavy.

'Look, Barbara, don't despair. These things happen from time to time. Why don't you come in and see me in a week or two?'

'Thanks, Jeff,' she said stiffly, trying to get off the phone before she choked on the threatened tears. 'I'm sorry to have disturbed you at this time of night.'

'That's quite all right.'

Jeff's voice was kind, sympathetic, but it didn't make the pain any easier to bear. It was all right for him. He had two grown-up children, and didn't have to go through the sort of pain she was going through.

She said goodbye and put the phone down. She felt numb. She had been so sure this time, so certain.

She leaned against the banister and buried her face in her hands. The make-up she had applied so carefully earlier ran in black streaks down her burning face, but she made no attempt to stop the rush of hot tears. She did not care.

She had never felt so unhappy in all her life! She would never have Adam's child, never, no matter what they said and, as she sobbed quietly, she heard Alison and Adam laughing together.

3

Adam stared at Barbara for a long while, his eyes narrowing. Lately, her behaviour had been puzzling, to say the least, and now . . .

It had been a long morning for him, starting at six. Lunch at home was supposed to be a treat before returning for what he knew would be a difficult afternoon. He was beginning to wish he hadn't bothered.

'I can't believe you're serious,' he said at last. 'You know what this dinner-dance means to me. It's imperative that you, as my wife, are there. I can't see why you won't come.'

'I'm sorry, Adam,' Barbara said unhappily. 'I have to have those roughs ready for Charles Latimer by the deadline. If I don't, apart from losing this contract, I'll also forfeit the good reputation I've been building up.'

'What about me? *My* position? *My* reputation?' he said, turning and pacing up and down the room. 'I've put up with your work, not to mention the time spent on this conservation business you've got yourself involved in. Doesn't our marriage mean anything to you?'

'Oh, Adam!' The colour drained from Barbara's face. 'How can you say that? You don't honestly believe I don't care, do you?'

'To be quite honest, Barbara, I don't know what to believe these days. I wouldn't mind if it was just your work, but it's the way you've climbed aboard this wildlife preservation band-wagon, almost against me.

'What's wrong with the people around here? Can't they see my proposed new developments will be good for the community? I'll be creating hundreds of jobs.'

'At what cost for future generations?' Barbara asked softly.

Adam poured himself a drink and sat

down opposite her, his expression softening a little.

'I'm sorry, darling,' he said. 'It's just that I hardly seem to see you at all these days. We never talk and, well, I seem to see more of Alison than I do of you!'

At the mention of Alison's name, Barbara's spirits slumped.

Alison, oh yes, Alison! She was always there, pushing Barbara farther and farther into the background, it seemed, just at a time when she already felt low about not being pregnant just yet.

She'd never told Adam about the false alarm over the pregnancy, feeling he had enough to contend with in his hectic business life, as well as the grief he'd felt over Tim's death and Alison's unhappiness. She'd spared him, but that meant she had to shoulder the burden of her disappointment all alone.

'Look at us now!' Adam's voice brought her thoughts back to their present argument. 'The first time we've had alone together for ages and we're bickering. And over what? A dinner-dance. Surely, Barbara, you could spare me just one evening? I wouldn't ask if it wasn't important to me.'

'I'll try, I promise, but I just don't know how this project is going to go. I'm at a really tricky stage right now and nothing I do seems to go right.'

'I know the feeling,' he said sympathetically. 'The harder you try, the worse things become. But there's something else, isn't there? This last week, you've been on edge. Whatever I say is wrong and I can't seem to do anything to please you, no matter how hard I try.'

She looked at him, aware of how much she really loved him. Surely she was wrong to be shutting him out?

'Oh, Adam, I'm sorry, it's just that . . . ' She faltered. 'I've been hoping, every month, wishing and hoping that this time I'll be pregnant. I do so want a baby!'

Tears welled up in her eyes as she tried so hard to find the right words to express all the emptiness she felt inside.

'I should have realised.' Adam put down his drink, untouched, and went to her, sitting beside her on the sofa and putting his arms around her sagging shoulders. 'I'm sorry, darling,' he said softly. 'I really should have thought of this.'

She wiped away her tears and smiled at him, a brave, wobbly smile which reminded him, somehow, of a little girl.

'That's my girl.' He grinned. 'I know how you feel. I'd love a baby, too, but it will happen when the time is right, you'll see. We'll have our family one day.'

'I love you so much, Adam,' Barbara said tenderly.

'What we need is to spend more time together,' he said, 'just you and I. This weekend should be good. We'll be on our own, with Alison away to her parents' for their ruby wedding anniversary and Gerry just refuses to stay here. He's booked into a local hotel.'

'He's very thoughtful,' Barbara said

quietly, 'always thinking of others.'

'We've got some pretty good friends, haven't we?' Adam leaned back and smiled. 'Take Alison! After all she's been through, she's still managed to work up enthusiasm for her parents' party. You'd think a wedding anniversary would upset her more than anything. All in all, she's pretty remarkable.'

Barbara tensed. Alison again! Why did she always have to crop up in *every* conversation?

'Talking of Alison,' Adam said thoughtfully, 'I don't know why I didn't think of it before. If you can't make it to the dinner-dance, I'm sure she'd be only too pleased to come in your place!'

Barbara shut her eyes tightly, forcing back tears of anger and resentment. The love, the warmth she had been surrounded in just a moment ago had vanished with Adam's enthusiastic suggestion.

★　★　★

Gerry stepped out of the bank and slipped his wallet carefully into his pocket, then looked up in time to see Alison across the street. She was hurrying along, holding tightly on to a large carrier bag.

'Alison!' he shouted, waving his arm and catching the attention of everyone in the street save the one person he wanted. 'Alison, wait!'

At last she heard him and her face broke into a smile.

'What brings you to town?' he asked, when he'd caught up with her.

'I've been looking for a present for my parents' wedding anniversary. It's this week-end and they're having a big family party. How about you? What are you up to?'

'I've just robbed the bank and now I thought I'd grab a bite to eat.' He grinned. 'I don't suppose you'd care to keep me company, would you?'

Alison glanced at her watch. There was still plenty of time before she was due at the hairdresser's.

'I'd love to,' she said, taking his arm.

The pub they chose was fairly quiet and Gerry found a small table tucked away at the back.

'It's nice in here, isn't it?' Alison said, her eyes shining brightly.

'I love these old-fashioned places,' Gerry agreed. 'There's so much atmosphere.'

Gradually, Alison felt herself warming to Gerry as they talked. No wonder Adam thought so much of him! He didn't have a bad word to say about anyone.

'How do you feel now?' he asked, as the barmaid served their meal and left.

'I'm fine.' She smiled. 'I'm really glad I came down here. It's done me the world of good.'

'I can see that,' he said. 'Adam was right to bring you here. It's not easy coping with something like that on your own. I should know.'

Alison looked thoughtfully at Gerry. He might be a happy-go-lucky man who liked to joke and have fun but, underneath, he was a very lonely man. He'd only been married for two years, he'd told her, when his wife had been killed in an accident.

They'd never had a family and, though it was more than twenty years ago, he'd never found anyone to take her place.

'That's why I was so pleased when Adam married Barbara,' Gerry was saying now. 'I suppose I envy him because I know how lucky he is. She's such a terrific girl, beautiful, clever, charming, and she adores him. Yes, he's a lucky man!'

Alison grimaced. Oh, yes, she was well aware of how wonderful Barbara was. In fact, it was rubbed in every time she saw her! She was graceful, beautiful and, yes, she appeared to adore Adam. But lately, Alison felt sure she could detect cracks beginning to appear in their perfect relationship.

'I'm sorry, Alison,' Gerry said suddenly. 'What a fool I am, I shouldn't be going on like this. You, of all people, must know how I feel and it's been far more recent for you, hasn't it?'

He'd seen her look and mistakenly believed that he'd revived painful memories for her. At the same time, Alison realised that her feelings must have been glaringly obvious. Gerry had saved her by giving her an ideal excuse. She had no alternative but to agree.

'You're right, Gerry,' she said. 'A sudden death is a terrible shock and hard to come to terms with, even if the love is no longer there.'

★   ★   ★

Gerry opened his mouth to speak, but her words had shocked him into silence. What on earth had she meant by that? Maybe she was just generalising, but her words had been spoken with such feeling, and perhaps a trace of bitterness, that he couldn't help wondering if she had been talking about herself.

As he watched her, a sad, wistful

expression clouded her eyes, one almost of longing.

'Alison,' he began.

'Oh, my goodness,' she said, brightening suddenly, 'look at the time! I'll be late for my appointment at the hairdresser's.'

She wouldn't, but she had noticed that Gerry was looking puzzled and she was afraid that she had already given too much away.

'I'm terribly sorry, Gerry, would you mind if I dashed off?'

'Of course not, it's been a pleasure.' He stood up, a bemused look in his eyes. 'Thank you for having lunch with me. I really enjoyed your company.'

'Me, too!' She smiled before gathering her things and hurrying off with a cheery farewell wave.

She was a vivacious, lively girl and he suspected that, underneath the confusion and sadness, lurked a fun-loving woman. He took a deep breath. No use thinking along those lines, he told himself grimly. There was at least ten years' difference in their ages, probably more. She wouldn't look twice at a guy his age!

★ ★ ★

Jess moved Nicola on to her hip and knocked softly at the study door before opening it. Jess coughed lightly and Barbara looked up at once, her frown of concentration fading as she saw Nicola.

'I'm sorry, love,' Jess said. 'I can see you're busy.' She looked despairingly at the waste paper littering the floor, and still toppling out of the overflowing bin. 'I've obviously caught you at a bad moment.'

'Every moment is a bad one for me just now, Jess,' Barbara said, moving away from her work and hurrying towards Jess with her arms outstretched. 'Hi, honey!'

She took Nicola and Jess could see how delighted she was when Nicola held tightly around Barbara's neck. Thank goodness Nicola loved Barbara so much! Jess had the feeling that her employer couldn't take much more rejection, real or imagined.

'You're working much too hard, Barbara,' Jess pointed out. 'I've come to see if I can drag you away for a coffee break.'

Barbara needed no persuading, happily carrying Nicola out of the study through to the kitchen.

'You haven't seen my gold chain anywhere, have you, Jess?'

'No, love.' Jess smiled. 'I'm sure it'll turn up when you're not really looking for it.'

Barbara looked edgy. 'Maybe, but it's just that, well, I've been looking for it for days. It was the first gift Adam ever bought me, you see.'

'Believe me,' Jess said, 'it'll be hiding behind a cushion or something. I'll have another look for it before I go, all right?'

'Thanks, Jess.' Barbara smiled and put Nicola down on a large rug in the centre of the kitchen where Jess had left some of her toys.

'There you are.' Jess placed a mug of coffee on the table for Barbara. 'It's instant, I'm afraid, but it's warm and wet and you look as if you could do with it. What's wrong, Barbara? I know you're upset about losing the chain, but there's more to it than that. You look very peaky. Do you feel all right?'

'Oh, Jess,' Barbara blurted out, unable to keep it inside any longer, 'I called the doctor last week and I was wrong. I'm *not* going to have a baby. It was just another false alarm. But I was so sure this time.'

'Oh, love, I am sorry. What a disappointment for you.'

Jess was at her side in an instant, her arms instinctively going out to hold her.

'You'll have your own baby one day,' Jess said encouragingly. 'I know you will. You'll hold a child of your own and you'll think back to now and wonder what on earth you'd been fretting about.'

'I wish I had half your strength, Jess,' Barbara said. 'I feel so useless. I don't know how you cope the way you do.'

'To be honest, Barbara, the only thing that really worries me right now is Nicola.'

Jess nodded at the child, who was now concentrating intently on feeding one of her dolls.

'I don't blame you,' Barbara said emotionally. 'When a child's health is on the line, everything else pales into insignificance. What did my doctor have to say? Any better news?'

'He's given her a thorough examination and he's going to do more tests.' Jess's voice failed her then, but she immediately tried to pull herself together, fighting back the tears. 'He's going to refer her to a specialist, if necessary. Oh, Barbara, I'm pleased something more's being done, but I'm just so worried about her.

'She's hardly more than a baby. Why should she be unwell and not just like any other normal little girl?'

Barbara put her hand consolingly on Jess's arm. 'I know, it's just not fair. But we must get to the bottom of what's making her sick so often. I'm sure it's nothing serious and, though it's easy for me to say, try not to worry too much.'

Jess blew her nose loudly, then picked up the empty mugs and put them in the sink. 'Right! Break over! Back to the grind!'

'It's all right,' Barbara said, hurrying to pick up Nicola. 'I'll carry her for you. Where are you going?'

'Upstairs,' Jess said. 'I have to do Alison's room.'

'I'll come up with you.' Barbara smiled. 'I have to collect some papers from the spare room,' she explained.

They hurried upstairs into Alison's room. Barbara put Nicola down on the floor and helped Jess strip the covers off the bed. Nicola toddled about the room, touching things, often chuckling with delight as she made new discoveries.

Jess was about to fetch clean sheets, when she caught sight of Nicola out of the corner of her eye. She was standing in front of the dressing-table and was patiently working Alison's small jewellery case towards the edge.

'No!' she cried out, but it was too late! With a cry of triumph, Nicola gave the box a last pull, bringing it crashing to the floor. It opened on impact, spilling jewellery all over the carpet.

Jess and Barbara stared at each other for a moment in shocked horror, then, realising nothing was broken and Nicola wasn't hurt, they both rushed forward to clear it up.

Barbara kneeled on the floor and began sorting through the tangle of chains until one, with a faulty clasp, caught her eye. She picked it up and examined it carefully. There could be no doubt. This was definitely her chain, the one she'd lost.

'What's my chain doing here?' Barbara said aloud, looking at Jess.

Jess shrugged and shook her head as she put the last of Alison's jewellery back into its box and placed it well out of Nicola's reach.

'Who knows what's going on inside that girl's head!' she said sadly.

At that moment, they heard the door slam downstairs and Barbara tightened her grip on the chain when she heard Alison's voice calling, 'Hello! Anyone home? It's only me!'

'Barbara, take it easy, please.'

Jess tried to restrain Barbara, who had leaped up and was heading for the door. She had never seen Barbara so angry before!

Alison was standing in the hall surrounded by carrier bags. She'd had her hair cut and looked almost radiant. When she saw Barbara hurrying downstairs towards her, she sensed at once that something was wrong.

Jess was hurrying behind, carrying her little girl in her arms and her face wore a worried expression. She paused for a moment at the bottom of the stairs, looking from Barbara to Alison, then hurried into the kitchen, closing the door behind her.

Alison's face fell when she saw the

gold chain dangling from Barbara's hand, even more so when she saw the look of black fury on Barbara's face. She'd completely forgotten to give it back to her after she'd found it!

'Oh, no!' She slapped her forehead dramatically. 'Oh, Barbara, I'm so sorry, how could I have forgotten? I found it on the landing the other night, just as I was going to bed, and I didn't want to disturb you, so I put it in my jewellery box for safe keeping.

'I meant to give it to you the next day, but I've had so much on my mind what with my parents' anniversary and everything . . . ' Her voice tailed away as Barbara continued to stare in obvious disbelief. 'I'm sorry. You must have thought you'd lost it for good.'

'How could you forget?' Barbara demanded. 'You wear jewellery every day. You must have seen it in your box. And the day after you arrived here, I told you how much it meant to me!'

'Look, Barbara.' Alison laughed nervously. 'What is this? I'm telling you the truth. You don't think I stole it?'

'You tell me!' Barbara declared hotly, almost shaking with rage. 'You know how much this means to me.'

'That's why I put it in my box,' Alison pointed out. 'You told me yourself that it had a faulty clasp. It must have fallen off as you went to bed.'

'And you kept it for days,' Barbara almost hissed. 'That's inexcusable.'

'I've apologised, haven't I?' Alison cried in exasperation. 'What more do you want? I thought I was doing you a favour. For goodness' sake, Barbara, I don't know what the big deal is. All this fuss over a little chain!'

Barbara was about to make an angry retort when Adam walked in.

'What's this?' he said, looking mystified. 'A hen party?'

Alison looked at Barbara. There was a strange look in her eyes and her voice was incredulous as she spoke.

'It's all rather silly, Adam,' she began. 'Barbara seems to think that I'm after her jewellery.'

Barbara wanted to speak, to say something in her defence, but her throat was tight and seemed to close around her words.

'The fact is,' Alison continued, 'I found her gold chain on the stairs and, knowing that it meant something to her, I put it in my jewel case for safe keeping.'

'But,' Barbara began, but Alison wasn't slow to seize the opportunity fate had handed her! 'It slipped my mind and now it seems that Barbara is accusing me of theft.'

It sounded so ridiculous the way Alison explained it! Adam turned to look at Barbara, a hardness coming into his tired eyes.

'Oh, for pity's sake, Barbara,' he said wearily, 'what on earth were you doing going through Alison's things?'

'I wasn't . . . I . . . '

Suddenly, it seemed to Barbara that the whole episode had been turned upside down and now it appeared to be all her fault. And the way Adam was looking at her now, it was clear he thought she was making a fuss over nothing. To him, she must look petty and silly.

'Well, you've got it back now,' he said coldly. 'I hope that's an end to it.'

Barbara looked at Alison, aware that her cheeks were burning with humiliation, and caught a strange expression on her adversary's face, a look of triumph? Maybe it was in Barbara's troubled mind, but there *had* been a look there, one she couldn't quite pin down, but one which chilled her to the bone.

Alison turned, picked up her bags with a flourish and flounced into the living room behind Adam.

'Would you like to see the dress I've bought for the party?' she said blithely. 'It's your favourite colour!'

Barbara's hands formed fists so tight that her nails dug hard into the palms of her hands. Turning furiously on her heel, she stormed into her study, slamming the door behind her.

*   *   *

Barbara picked up the blouses Jess had just finished ironing and draped them carefully over her arm.

'I'll take these up to Alison's room,' she said. 'It will give me a chance to apologise about yesterday!'

Jess pulled a face at the thought but said nothing, realising it would be better for Barbara to make her peace than go on fighting. She knocked lightly on Alison's door and didn't enter until Alison called out. She looked surprised to see Barbara.

'I've brought these up for you,' she explained. 'Jess has just ironed them. They're still warm.' She laughed nervously.

'Thanks, Barbara.' Alison took the blouses.

Was it a deliberate gesture when Alison turned her back completely on Barbara, as if dismissing her?

'I also wanted to apologise,' Barbara rushed on, 'about yesterday. It's no excuse, but I guess I've been working a little too hard lately and I seem to be operating on a pretty short fuse!'

'It's forgotten,' Alison said, reaching in the wardrobe for hangers.

Barbara was slightly taken aback. Alison's manner still seemed off-hand and she had made no attempt to apologise herself.

'You're going to your parents' on Saturday, aren't you?' Barbara tried to be friendly again.

She could hear the effort straining her voice and wondered if Alison realised just how much courage it had taken to come up to her room and humble herself like this.

'Saturday afternoon, yes,' Alison said. 'The party is on Sunday, but I want to be there the night before so I can help arrange things.'

'How are you getting there?' Barbara went on.

'By train.'

'You could take my car. My insurance covers any driver,' Barbara suggested on the spur of the moment. It was an ideal way of making up, a sincere offer, out of friendship. 'I won't be needing it myself. I'm going to a meeting on Saturday night, but it's my turn to get a lift and Adam will be working, so, it's all yours if you want it.'

'Are you sure?' Alison said, for the first time smiling a genuine smile as she carefully packed her parents' present in its box. 'Actually, I'd rather drive. I don't like going on the train. Thank you, it's very good of you and I'd like to take you up on your offer.'

'Well, that's settled then,' Barbara declared, feeling a lot better. 'Want a hand with your packing?'

Alison smiled briefly and nodded and, an uneasy truce having been arrived at, the two women set about finishing the chore.

★   ★   ★

It was pointless trying to work. Adam had been sitting at his desk for over an hour. Everyone else had gone.

It had been a hectic week, with early starts and late nights and, with the friction at home, he was almost at the end of his tether. He was so tired, he could hardly think straight. He decided to head on home.

As he drove, he remembered that Barbara wouldn't be there. She'd be at a meeting with her fellow conservationists. The thought added to his gloom, for she was a member of the very group *causing* his extra work and headaches.

He let himself into the house, now strangely quiet. He hung up his jacket and went into the kitchen to make coffee, then carried it, strong and black, into the living room, where he slipped a tape into the deck.

He couldn't remember the last time he'd been able to relax like this, but the tape had barely started when the telephone rang. Reluctantly, he picked it up.

'Adam. Oh, thank goodness!'

'Alison?'

'I've been trying to get hold of you at the office, but all I got was that wretched answering machine!'

'Is something wrong?'

'Yes,' she said. 'Barbara's car has broken down.'

'Where are you?'

'I'm at a hotel. I'm sorry to call you, Adam, but I didn't know what else to do. I'm not on a bus route and the garage repair people say they'll be at least an hour, maybe more.'

'I'll come and get you,' Adam said. 'I can take you straight to the station.'

'Thanks, Adam. I knew I could rely on you.' Alison sounded near to tears. 'I did so want to get to my parents' place tonight.'

'And you will! Don't worry, I'll be right with you. What's the name of the hotel?'

Twenty minutes later, Adam pulled up by the hotel and saw Alison pacing up and down outside. He leaned over to open the door and she climbed in.

'Where's Barbara's car?'

'Down that way.' She pointed back along the country road. 'The breakdown man came, but he says it will have to be towed away. I'm sorry, Adam, but it seems to be something pretty serious.' She handed him a card. 'That's where they're taking it. You're to call them in the morning.'

'Thanks.' He pocketed the card without looking at it. 'Did you leave your luggage in the hotel?'

She nodded and he got out of the car and went inside to collect it. Coming back, he suggested, 'Would you like to have a meal somewhere to kill the time before your train's due? I don't know about you, but I haven't eaten yet.'

'I'm starving,' Alison admitted with a wry smile. 'And a bit cold.' She rubbed her bare arms with her hands. 'It's a bit chilly and I wasn't expecting to walk anywhere!'

It wasn't only the cool air making her shiver, though. Once again, she was going to have Adam all to herself and this time they were having a meal together. Given this second chance, she knew she mustn't foul things up!

'We may as well go back to town,' he said, starting the car. 'So I can be sure of getting you to the station on time.'

'I thought you were supposed to be working tonight,' Alison commented.

'I was. Couldn't concentrate on anything, though, so I gave up in the end. Once we've got the go-ahead for the new training centre, things should calm down.'

'Training centre?'

'We need somewhere to run residential courses for our systems. Most of the big companies have them now.'

'So what's the problem?'

'The local conservation society.' He pulled a face. 'They don't want the country-side ruined by new buildings!'

'Isn't Barbara..?'

'Yes.' he said shortly, and Alison smiled inwardly when she saw the hardness of his jaw at the mention of his wife's name.

He parked the car at the back of a

large hotel and led Alison into the restaurant. She noticed how quickly he seemed able to relax and coaxed him into talking about his worries at work, offering the sympathetic ear his wife had foolishly been denying him.

It was a crime that a man like Adam should spend so much time being hassled and worried. Barbara didn't deserve him!

* * *

Barbara walked into the bar with the others, her posters rolled tightly under her arm, protected by a layer of thin card.

'You've done a marvellous job on those posters, Barbara.' Bob Jenkins, the conservationist spokesman, patted her shoulder. 'I'm sure it was your artwork that attracted so many people to tonight's meeting. Those posters you have there should clinch it for the campaign.'

'But do you really think we can win,

Bob?' she said softly. 'It seems doubtful to me.'

'Even if we don't, at least we'll have tried!' He turned towards the bar and ordered drinks for everyone.

She took her drink from Bob and moved away from the others slightly, wanting her own space, her own quiet corner for a few minutes, and it was then that she saw the familiar figure through the French doors, sitting in the restaurant adjacent to the bar.

It was Adam! But what was he doing here? He was obviously talking to someone across the table from him. But *who* was with him? She looked at the others. They were deep in conversation and argument, enabling her to move closer to the French doors.

Now, she could see Adam's companion. No! It was impossible! Alison was supposed to be well on her way to her parents by now and Adam was supposed to be working late at the office. They had *both* lied to her, *deceived* her!

The hubbub around her faded and the vision of Adam and Alison sharpened before her eyes. Their heads were close together, too close, and she felt sure she could hear Adam's deep, warm laughter and Alison's flirtatious giggle even through the glass doors.

She swayed on her feet and reached out for a small table to stop herself keeling right over. What was going on? What was happening to her? She just couldn't believe what she was seeing.

Tears misted her eyes and the sight of Alison and Adam sitting together blurred in front of her. She wanted to turn away and join her friends at the bar, pretending she had never witnessed this cruel betrayal.

The way Alison was gazing at Adam . . . had it been anyone else but Adam, Barbara felt it would be delightful to see.

She watched as Adam put his arm around Alison's waist and led her towards the door opposite the French doors. He opened the door and Alison slipped her arm through his and it was like this that Barbara watched them leave the restaurant, arm in arm, like husband and wife — or like lovers!

'Another drink, Barbara?' Bob said beside her.

Despite the threatening tears, she had to hold on to herself. She mustn't lose her grip now.

'Are you all right? You look as if you've seen a ghost? Barbara . . . '

Her life was falling apart and she was helpless to stop it. Her work was going badly and now it seemed she was losing her husband as well.

She began to tremble. What on earth was she going to do?

4

Adam drew the car to a stop outside the railway station, leaned his arm on the steering-wheel and peered out through the windscreen.

'Train shouldn't be long now,' he murmured.

'You'll be glad to see the back of me, I'll bet,' Alison remarked sadly, watching Adam.

She saw his jaw tighten as she went on.

'I know Barbara will, anyway. I suppose it's the strain of having me around all the time, but she seems really up tight just now. I guess you need some time on your own. It's been a bit of a strain for me, too. I just wish I knew what I'd done to make her dislike me so much.'

She said the last sentence so unhappily that Adam turned to look at her, appalled to see the sorrow in her eyes.

'Alison, don't be ridiculous,' he said, grasping her hand tightly. 'It's been terrific having you around. You can't imagine how much I've enjoyed talking over old times and, well, thinking about Tim again.

'As for the business about the necklace . . . ' He shook his head as if he still didn't understand quite what had gone wrong. 'Barbara was totally in the wrong about that. Don't worry too much about what she says. I think she's been working and worrying too much.'

Alison felt a sudden surge of confidence. So Barbara had failed to convince him that she'd made a genuine mistake! She could see the thin cracks getting even wider now. She hated herself for it, but she so desperately wanted Adam.

'Anyway, Adam,' she said, her voice trembling as she fought back tears, 'I hate to be the cause of so much ill-feeling. I don't want to cause any further trouble. It isn't fair on Barbara. So, I think I'll stay on with my parents for the rest of the holiday.'

She looked down at her lap, twisting and turning her fingers together nervously. 'They'd be happy to let me have my old room for a while.'

Adam had never seen her looking so crestfallen and unhappy, except perhaps once and that was a long time ago, and it had been his fault then.

'I want you to stay, Alison,' he said hoarsely, his voice rough with pity and remorse.

For a moment, they looked at each other and it seemed to Alison as if they were the only two people in the world. But the Tannoy on the station suddenly crackled into life and an announcement came through, ending the magic for the time being.

'Sounds like your train.' Adam grinned and jumped out of the car, hurrying round to open Alison's door for her.

On the platform, he set down her

case and hugged her, hoping to cheer her up and make her realise she wasn't the burden she seemed to think. When she turned her face up to look at him, it seemed only natural to give her a brotherly kiss to reinforce how fond he was of her.

But the kiss he had aimed at her cheek somehow found its way to her mouth, and his lips lingered there longer than he had intended.

As they pulled apart, the train whooshed in beside them, but they were oblivious to everything around them. For an instant, Alison had caught Adam off guard and seen something in his eyes she never expected to see again.

He was no less surprised at the strength of *his* feelings! He looked at Alison with flushed cheeks and bright eyes. She had always been pretty, but the years had added something special. Now, she was beautiful, radiant, almost.

And that one kiss had brought a thousand memories rushing back. He smiled and let her go, stooping to pick up her overnight case. His reaction to her kiss had been no more than a fleeting, though disturbing, thought and he tried to dismiss it as no more than that.

'Ready, then?' he asked with false brightness, opening the carriage door.

Alison hurried on to the train just as it was starting off. She looked back through the open window of the carriage door. Adam was standing there with a sad look in his eyes.

Her own eyes suddenly filled with tears, but they were tears of joy. For she knew now that the happiness they'd once shared could be theirs again!

* * *

Thank godness I'm home, Barbara thought, closing the front door firmly behind her and stumbling through to the lounge. At least *here* I don't have to go on pretending. She still didn't know how she'd survived the rest of the evening after seeing Alison and Adam together.

She flicked on as many lights as she could, threw down her bag and then went through to the kitchen to make herself a coffee. Trembling, and with a bad headache coming on, she went into the lounge. Her eyes immediately fastened on the framed wedding photograph taken in her parents' sunny Californian garden. Garlands of flowers hung everywhere and, in the centre of it all, beneath an ornate arbour, stood the loving couple.

Looking at them now, those happy, carefree faces, Barbara found it hard to believe they were the same people. She turned away abruptly as tears suddenly blurred the picture.

What had happened to their lives? They had been so full of hope and plans — and love, almost as if they shared the same mind and soul. They had laughed, loved and cried together, *always together!* But now they seemed far apart and were growing even farther apart with every passing day. She pressed her hand to her forehead, trying to figure out what had gone so terribly wrong.

She could find only one answer — Alison!

Things had been fine until *she'd* arrived! Her stomach felt as if it were in knots, twisting and turning. It was Alison's fault. And Adam, too, had been practically falling over himself in an effort to be nice to her since she'd arrived.

But it was her fault, too. She'd left them alone together too much. She'd practically forced them together! The hall clock chimed and Barbara realised it was midnight. She looked up and around the empty room. Adam was still not home and he'd left the restaurant with Alison hours ago! She stood up and marched towards the stairs, gripping the banister rail as if her life depended on it, her unhappy mind torturing her, reminding her that Adam was with Alison, right now.

They were together, and she was alone!

Barbara felt she'd been tossing and turning for hours when, at last, she heard a car pull up outside, then the front door slam as Adam let himself in.

She was suddenly awake, listening hard as he moved about downstairs, turning off lights and checking the locks. Then he was coming up the stairs. The thought made her tremble. She wasn't sure she could face him yet.

She burrowed down beneath the covers and hid her face in her pillow, her whole body tense with nervous exhaustion.

Adam came quietly into the room, tiptoeing across the floor and switching on a table lamp, obviously getting undressed as quickly as he could. He came over to the bed.

'Are you awake, Barbara?' he whispered.

He sat down beside her and reached out, his hand touching her shoulder lightly. She flinched away, unable to prevent her whole body from stiffening completely. The thought of him and Alison together . . .

'Barbara? I know you're awake, and I don't blame you for not speaking to me, but there's a perfectly simple explanation for why I'm so late!

'I got a call from Alison earlier on. Your car broke down and she was stranded in the middle of nowhere! So I picked her up and saw her on to the train. Just an old-fashioned act of chivalry.'

Barbara sat up then, holding the covers tightly around her, glaring at him, almost shaking with suppressed fury.

'Oh, really!' she said drily, only too aware of the bitterness in her voice. 'Is that what they call it around here?'

'Call what? What are you talking about?' he said lightly, trying, she was sure, to look innocent.

She didn't reply and Adam swallowed nervously. He couldn't help it, but Barbara was making him feel guilty.

Yet he had nothing to feel guilty about. He hadn't done anything wrong, but Barbara was acting as if . . .

'The garage is keeping your car to work on it.' He tried to make light of the situation. 'You'll be glad to know Alison got on the train all right.'

Barbara did not return his smile, though. For pity's sake, don't say anything else, she thought. If I hear Alison's name mentioned once more . . .

'What's bugging you?' he said at last in exasperation. 'Is something wrong?'

'*Should* something be wrong?' she threw back at him.

Adam ran his fingers through his hair, his patience finally running out. Barbara was obviously spoiling for a fight.

'OK, now what am I supposed to have done?' he shouted, more with frustration than anger.

'You tell me!'

Barbara got out of bed, her face blazing red as she finally gave full vent to her feelings.

'So you gave Alison a lift, did you? What about the rest, Adam? The bits you've conveniently forgotten to mention. What about the cosy, intimate, little scene at the hotel? I saw you, arm-in-arm with that . . . that . . . '

Adam faltered at this accusation, realising suddenly how compromising it must have looked. He had never seen Barbara as upset and angry as now and didn't know how to react.

'She had a long wait for the train. I couldn't just leave her to sit in the station,' he said, cursing himself for being a fool.

He had been wrong not to mention straight away that they'd had dinner together. Now, it looked as if he was trying to hide something!

'Of course you couldn't,' Barbara said acidly. 'So you decided to entertain her instead.'

He wasn't sure what he'd meant or intended any more. Barbara was twisting his words, tripping him up at every opportunity.

'But then, of course, you wouldn't expect anyone to see you, would you?' She stopped pacing the floor and stood in front of him, staring down at him. 'You and *her*!' She couldn't even bring herself to say her name.

'We had a meal, that's all. Why all the fuss?' He laughed humourlessly.

'Oh, come off it, Adam!' she flung at him, turning her back and storming over to the window. 'I wasn't born yesterday.'

'*Nothing happened*!' he insisted, getting quickly off the bed and reaching out to her. 'Why don't you believe me?'

'Don't insult me with your lies.' She moved away from him. 'You arranged the whole thing, didn't you? You thought I'd be safely out of the way at my meeting. Did you bring her back here, Adam? Well, did you?'

'Is that how your mind works?' he said, his voice low and angry. 'I can't believe you're saying these things. It's me, Adam, you're talking to!'

He was hurt that she didn't trust

him, but felt a stab of guilt as he remembered the goodnight kiss and the sudden realisation that he still found Alison desirable.

'It's all too convenient, Adam,' she said softly, sitting down on the edge of the bed, all the fight suddenly leaving her. She looked exhausted, her eyes red and swollen against her pale, anxious face.

But Adam's anger was too great, now, to see how upset she was.

'You've got a warped mind, Barbara,' he flung at her, storming off towards the spare bedroom, stopping only to shout over his shoulder. 'With that imagination, you should be writing gossip columns.'

But, even in the spare room, sleep eluded him. He stared at the ceiling, deep in thought. What had happened to them? Their marriage had been so good, so harmonious, until recently. Home had been a peaceful haven and now it was just another area of conflict and aggression, no longer a happy escape from work.

Where had all the dreams gone? What had become of the children they hoped to raise? Maybe a baby would have made a difference? He turned over and ran his hand over the cold, empty space in the bed, a yawning gulf which was going to be hard to fill.

If things go on like this, he thought dully, just before drifting into an uneasy sleep, there never will be a baby to help heal the rift.

When Barbara eventually woke, she ran her hand over the covers on Adam's side of the bed and put her head on his pillow, needing the comfort that brought her.

She glanced in the mirror when she got up and pulled a face. She had never seen herself looking so awful. Pulling on her dressing-gown, she went downstairs to make coffee. She sat down at the kitchen table to sip it, black and unsweetened. Adam had obviously left for the office.

The clock ticking loudly on the wall

drew her attention to the time. Jess was late this morning. Suddenly, she heard a car pull up outside and footsteps running to the back of the house. She half stood, her first thoughts of Adam. Had he come home from work? Were they going to make up? She held her breath, waiting.

The back door flew open and Jess rushed in, distraught, tears streaming down her colourless face and her hair all over the place.

'Jess!' Barbara ran over to her, grabbing her tightly as if she could squeeze the hurt out of her.

'What's happened?'

'It's Nicola!' Jess managed to say between sobs, and Barbara felt an icy ball form in her stomach.

Jess took a few deep breaths, sobbing and gulping as she tried to control herself. 'She was taken ill in the night, a terrible bout of sickness. She was burning up. We had to call an ambulance. Oh, Barbara, I was so scared.

'The doctors say she's stable now. She should be all right, but they don't know what caused the attack or if it's likely to happen again. It could be months or . . . or . . . Oh, Barbara, I can't stand it.'

'Where are you going now?' Barbara asked anxiously, afraid Jess was going to break down completely. She'd never seen her so distraught.

'The taxi's waiting outside. I'm going home to fetch some things for Nicola. She left her old rabbit behind and the nurse said she should have something familiar with her.' She smiled sadly.

'And I've got to let Pete and the kids know what's happening. Then I'm going straight back to the hospital. I just dropped by to let you know that I wouldn't be in this morning. I'm sorry, Barbara.'

'Give me five minutes, Jess,' Barbara said firmly, steering her towards the door. 'Go and tell the taxi driver to wait. I'm coming with you. Go on now, Jess.'

When they arrived at the hospital, Jess took Barbara straight to the ward where Nicola still lay, sleeping and sedated. Barbara looked down at her and her eyes filled with tears.

She reached out and held one tiny white hand. Barbara looked at the drip running into Nicola's other hand, and swallowed hard. All that equipment looked so big in comparison to the tiny child in the bed, so small and helpless.

But she wasn't alone, not when she had so many who loved her and wanted her to get better.

With this strengthening thought, Barbara turned to Jess, who was in such distress, and realised that her own problems were trivial compared to what Jess was facing right now. If only the doctors could find out what brought on little Nicola's attacks.

'I'm going to talk to the doctor,' Barbara said suddenly.

'Thanks, Barbara.' Jess covered her hand with her own. 'He told me something, but I didn't really take it in.

I was still reeling.'

Five minutes later, the doctor was with her.

'Hello.' He smiled warmly. 'You're here with Mrs Wheeler, I understand. My name is Redbridge, James Redbridge.'

'I really want to help,' Barbara said candidly, sounding very cool and controlled. 'Is Nicola very ill? Jess seems somehow to think she is.'

'I'm afraid so,' he said honestly, his face lining with sadness. 'We have the results of some tests her own doctor was running and we've done some of our own. It doesn't look too good.'

Barbara felt as if she'd been punched in the stomach, but whatever she felt inside, she was determined, for Jess's sake, to keep her control. 'Go on,' she said in a subdued voice.

'Nicola has a rare blood disorder,' he said sadly. 'One which has only recently been identified. As yet, it hasn't even got a name, just an official number.'

'What about treatment?' Barbara

demanded. 'What's being done?'

He looked away, obviously discon-
certed. 'I'm afraid I have to tell you
what I told Mrs Wheeler. There is
research going on at the moment and a
new drug, developed in America, has
been tested on adults with a similar
blood disorder to Nicola's.

'It hasn't been successful in all
cases, but the results are encouraging.
They've only just begun trying it out on
some desperately-ill American children.
Again, the results have been mixed.'

Barbara looked thoughtfully at the
doctor, ready to clutch at any strand of
hope, however fragile, that he was able
to offer her.

'They're light years ahead of us over
there. A brilliant specialist, Dr Horrell,
has set up a clinic specifically to treat
children like Nicola. The drugs he uses
are very different to ours, but he's had
some amazing results and combines the
drugs with diet and therapy.

'We could send Nicola there, but it
would be expensive and I know that Mr

Wheeler is out of work. How can I tell these people that a possible cure is ready and waiting for their daughter when I know they can't afford to pay for it? But, without it, little Nicola's chances of a normal, healthy life are slim.'

He looked so torn apart by his own helplessness that Barbara felt her heart go out to him. How awful to have to tell parents their child might be a permanent invalid or even die, when he knew all the time that money could possibly buy the cure.

'Yes, Doctor, it so often comes down to lack of money these days! Look, could you make the necessary arrangements to contact this specialist? If he'll take her case, we'll fly Nicola out to the States as soon as possible,' Barbara said with sudden determination.

'I'll pay the bill. Money's no problem. She must have the very best. Can you arrange it?'

Momentarily, he was taken aback, then his face lit up and he began to shake her hand, pumping it up and down until her arm ached.

'Yes, yes, I can do that, but are you sure about this? I'm talking about thousands of pounds, and you must remember there's no guarantee the treatment will be successful.'

'She's worth it,' Barbara said quietly. 'And we have at least to try, don't we? Anyway, Doctor, if you'll excuse me,' Barbara said then, standing up to go. 'I'll go and tell Jess.'

Jess was sitting beside the bed, holding Nicola's hand and gazing down at her, tears just behind her eyes. She was singing softly to the little girl, her voice breaking every so often as emotion overcame her. Barbara crept up behind her and touched her shoulder gently.

'Come outside and have a coffee, Jess,' she whispered. 'The nurse will sit with Nicola. I have something to tell you.'

Outside in the corridor, Barbara brought two coffees from the machine and handed one to Jess. 'Sit down,' she said. 'Hopefully, I've some better news.'

She started to tell Jess what the doctor had said.

'That's more or less what he told me,' Jess nodded. 'Except the bit about America. If only there were some way of raising the money . . . a bank loan, or a special fund for Nicola to raise money from the public. I'd sell my soul if necessary!'

'There's no need to go quite that far.' Barbara smiled. 'Right now the doctor is trying to make arrangements to send Nicola to the States, and you'll go with her!'

Jess looked confused, hardly daring to believe what Barbara was saying. 'How?' she cried anxiously.

'I'll see to the bill,' Barbara said. 'I've told you this a hundred times, Jess. I *want* to help. I love Nicola and I won't sit by and watch her suffer needlessly, not when I have the means to help her.'

'Oh, Barbara.' Jess put her coffee down on the seat beside her and hugged Barbara, tears of relief coursing down her face. There was hope again! 'I don't know how to thank you. You've already done so much.'

She mopped her tears with a tissue, then turned to smile at Barbara.

'What kind of friend would I be if I didn't help?' Barbara asked simply. 'Shall we go back in now?'

The nurse stood up when they entered the ward, smiling warmly. 'She seems to be rallying a little,' she told them and, at that point, the doctor came in.

'Could I have a word with you, Mrs Wheeler?' His manner now was much more positive. 'I've been making some phone calls. The wheels are in motion!'

★ ★ ★

Alison paid the taxi driver and stood on the path looking up at the house for a moment — Adam's house! Somehow, she felt as if she were coming home and knew it was because he lived there and

118

she belonged with him, wherever he was.

She picked up her case and strode towards the house, confident and happy, unaware of Barbara at an upstairs window, watching her every movement.

She opened the door and let herself into the hall, taking a deep, happy breath and smiling when she saw Adam's jacket hanging on the stand. Her heart fluttered and she suppressed an urge to go over and touch it.

She couldn't stop smiling and she knew it was because she was going to see Adam again. Every moment away from him had been miserable. All she'd thought of, despite the party and meeting her family and friends again, was this moment, the sweet moment of coming back to Adam.

She looked up the stairs to the landing, still smiling, but it faded quickly when she saw Barbara standing there. Why did she have to ruin everything?

Almost in the same instant, Alison noticed the look on Barbara's face. There was something different about her. She looked more confident, more sure of herself somehow. Then Alison noticed something else — her own suitcases at Barbara's feet! She dropped her week-end bag on the floor. What on earth was Barbara playing at?

Barbara began to descend the stairs, a case in each hand, slowly, calmly, her head high, her back straight, her face a fixed mask of complete control, betraying nothing of what she felt.

Alison watched, her heart racing, not wanting to meet Barbara's eyes.

'Don't bother to make yourself at home again, Alison,' she said, her voice as sharp as a razor edge. 'I've packed all your belongings for you, to save you the trouble. You've outstayed your welcome and I want you out of my house, and out of my life!'

Barbara's voice was strong and controlled, with the certainty that what she was doing was right. Alison just stared at her cases, unable to speak, not knowing what to do. She looked into Barbara's eyes and was chilled by what she saw there. There was no doubt. Barbara meant business. She really was throwing her out, and after all Adam had said!

'Shall I help you to the door,' Barbara asked politely, 'or can you manage?'

'I'll manage.' Alison's voice was hardly more than a whisper. Then she picked up her cases and struggled towards the door, which Barbara hurried to hold open for her.

She gave Barbara a quick, bewildered look before walking back out into the early-evening sunshine. Behind her, she heard the door close firmly and she turned round once to look back at the house, before struggling unsteadily down the path, the cases bumping against her legs.

Inside the house, Barbara leaned against the door and closed her eyes. She took several deep breaths then smiled with the pure relief that it was over. Alison had finally gone.

With her out of the way, and Nicola's trip to America coming up, it would give her time to think if she and Adam had much of a future together.

She held out her hands in front of her and looked down at them, surprised to see how much they were shaking.

5

Alison paid the taxi driver and waited until he had driven away before picking up her suitcase and turning into the office building. She only hoped she was in time and that Adam hadn't left for home yet.

She still hadn't been able to take in what had happened. Barbara had always appeared so weak, Alison couldn't believe she'd actually had the guts to turn her out.

Inside the wide foyer of the modern, impressive-looking building, she approached the security man and asked him to check if Mr Simmons was still in his office. The man looked at her curiously and lifted the desk phone.

'Mr Simmons?' he queried. 'There's a Mrs Johnstone here to see you. She has her luggage with her, sir.'

Upstairs, Adam frowned and drummed

his fingers on his desk. What on earth was Alison doing here? Surely it would have been more sensible of her to go straight to the house?

'Ask her to come up, would you please, Sam?' he said at last. 'Get her to leave her things at Reception.'

Alison thanked the man and hurried towards the lift. How on earth was she going to explain all this to Adam?

Adam met her out of the lift and saw at once that something was wrong. She looked very close to tears.

'Alison, what's happened?' He drew her into his office and led her towards a chair.

'Oh, Adam.' Her lower lip trembled. 'I don't know what I've done this time. It's Barbara. She's . . . she's . . . Oh, Adam, when I got back to the house, she'd packed my things, then she told me to leave.'

Adam could only stare at Alison in disbelief, but he felt his anger rising. What on earth had brought this on? Surely Barbara still didn't believe that there was something going on between himself and Alison?

Alison, distraughtly screwing a tissue in her fingers, went on in a tearful voice. 'I don't know what's going on. I feel so guilty causing all this trouble. If only I knew what I'd done.'

'You haven't done anything,' Adam said, his heart going out to Alison. She looked so helpless.

How *dare* Barbara behave like this towards Alison, a guest in their house and one of his dearest friends! What was she playing at?

'I didn't know where else to go,' Alison said, gulping back her sobs. 'I didn't want to go back to my parents without first telling you why . . . '

'You were right to come here,' he assured her gently. 'Look, we've a flat on the top floor here which we use for visiting VIPs. No-one's in it at the moment, so it's all yours.'

'Thank you, Adam.' She smiled and he was relieved to see some of the anxiety fade from her eyes.

'Come on. We may as well go straight up there now and get you settled.'

'Like it?' Adam grinned as he opened the door of the executive flat with a flourish.

'It's fabulous!' Alison felt over-whelmed as she looked around the beautiful living room.

'And it's all ready for you,' he said.

'Oh, Adam, I'm sorry to be such a nuisance.' She clasped his hands. 'It seems that you're always running around after me for one reason or another, and I'm so grateful.'

'I don't mind one bit,' he assured her. 'But now,' he glanced at his watch, 'I'm going to go and sort this nonsense out once and for all.'

He let go of her hands and trailed his fingers across her cheek, allowing his eyes to linger on her face. 'And don't worry,' he said tenderly, 'I'll be back!'

Alison rushed to the window and watched until he appeared in the car park below, striding towards his car.

This was working out far better than she'd dreamed! She wouldn't like to be in Barbara's shoes when he got home. And he said he was coming back, *coming back to her!*

His car pulled away smoothly and she waited until it was out of sight, then ran to unpack her case. She hadn't a single moment to waste!

She had to be ready when he returned and, this time, there would be no mistakes. This time, she wouldn't let him go . . .

* * *

Adam stormed towards his house. He was furious now! The closer he'd come to home, the angrier he'd become. He kept picturing Alison arriving at Starlings Corner only to suffer the degradation of being thrown out!

Barbara had a lot to answer for and he meant to see that he got some answers!

He stormed in, slamming the door

behind him. 'Barbara!' he shouted. 'Where are you?'

'In here!'

Adam strode purposefully into the lounge and was about to speak when he realised that Barbara was on the telephone and writing something down. She glanced up at him briefly but went on talking.

Her manner was brisk and efficient, not what he had been expecting at all. And only now did he see the two suitcases standing at her feet.

She looked at him again, but didn't smile, even when she saw his puzzled expression at the sight of her cases. Where was she going? Surely she wasn't leaving him, he thought suddenly, his anger giving way a little to uncertain, confusing emotions.

At last she put down the telephone and turned to look at him steadily, her eyes unwavering.

'What's going on?' he said, staring pointedly at the cases.

'I'm going to the States,' she said

briskly and, for a moment, he felt as if he were talking to a total stranger. She was pale, but totally in control and there was no hint of the volatility of the past few days.

He could hardly believe that this was the same person who had ranted at him for having a meal with Alison!

'To America?' he said. 'But why, Barbara?'

'If you really want to know, I'm taking Jess and Nicola to a clinic in California,' she said calmly. 'Nicola's illness has taken a turn for the worse and it's vital that she receives the right treatment as quickly as possible, and it's only available in the States!'

Adam reached out and held on to the back of a chair, his head spinning as he realised that Barbara was not, after all, walking out on him. But his relief at this was overshadowed by the gravity of little Nicola's illness.

'I'm sorry to hear that,' he said, trying to force himself to think rationally. 'How long will you be gone?

Where will you stay?'

'I can't say for sure,' she explained. 'It all depends on how quickly Dr Horrell can see us. He's a very busy man and there are so many children needing his skills. It's a long shot, Adam, but we're going to try. We have to. We're taking it one step at a time and the first thing is to get Nicola into that clinic and properly assessed.'

Adam stared at Barbara for a long time. He knew how much little Nicola meant to her, but this strength and self-control was something in Barbara he'd never seen before.

'I hope it goes well,' he said, feeling that his words were so inadequate under the circumatances. 'You know I'll miss you,' he added awkwardly, his voice barely audible.

Barbara looked at him, her eyebrows raised in surprise. She had never heard him sound unsure of himself before!

'Will you?' she asked coldly. 'I doubt it! I'm quite relieved to be going actually. It will give me a chance to think about us, and about our marriage!'

She looked at him dispassionately and went on. 'Let's be honest with ourselves, Adam. Things haven't been very good between us lately, have they? Of course, I also want to spend some time with my parents. I'm sure I'll be made welcome *there*!'

This last remark was spoken with such feeling that Adam felt himself shiver. He wanted to say he didn't know what she was talking about, but that would have been a lie.

'And you needn't expect to see Alison back here,' Barbara went on. 'I told her to leave, and I meant it! I don't want that woman in my house any longer, Adam. I know she's been going through a hard time lately, but now it's high time she stood on her own two feet!'

She stared intently at him, her bright eyes holding a challenge. But he was too weary, too stunned, to rise to the bait.

'I know all about it,' he said, sighing. 'Alison came to the office. That's why I came home. I wanted to talk this through. I don't know what's been going on between you and Alison, but . . .'

'Don't you?' she interrupted. 'I find it very hard to believe you could be so naive. But perhaps it doesn't matter any more, one way or the other. What's important right now, is that I get Nicola into that clinic.'

Adam didn't want her to go, but knew she must for Nicola's sake. Suddenly, he began to realise just how much he loved and needed her, but the atmosphere between them was far too strained for him to put his feelings properly into words.

'Can I run you to the airport?' he asked lamely.

'I've called a cab,' she said, briskly, 'and that sounds like it now!'

Adam went for her cases, but she beat him to it. Picking them up, she hurried towards the door. He stood back uselessly. She didn't need him now, that was obvious.

'Barbara, I . . . '

'There's nothing left for us to talk about now, Adam,' she said and there was no relenting in her attitude.

He bent forward intending to kiss her goodbye, but she turned her head away. He drew back, already feeling a sense of loss — no goodbye kiss, no hint of love or affection! Yet Barbara had always been so loving and demonstrative in the past. He felt a momentary pang of guilt. Had *he* done this to her?

'Give my love to your parents,' he said quickly, as the taxi driver revved the engine impatiently. 'Let me know how it goes!'

But Barbara was already in the taxi and, as it drew away, he noticed she didn't even look back once!

Adam stood in the drive, and watched as the taxi disappeared into the distance, too stunned to move. The argument he had been ready for had never happened. Something far worse had occurred instead!

He turned to go back into the house when another car turned the corner and swept up the drive. Gerry leaped out, all smiles as he slapped Adam heartily on the shoulder. Adam just stared.

'Hi, Adam!' He grinned. 'How goes it? Was that Barbara in the cab?'

'Oh, hello, Gerry,' Adam said solemnly. 'Yes, it was Barbara.'

'So why the long face?' Gerry asked.

'It's a long story,' Adam said grimly. 'Come on in and I'll tell you about it over a drink!'

* * *

Alison twirled around in front of the cheval mirror, quivering with suppressed excitement. The dress she had bought for her parents' anniversary was perfect for tonight, for she had bought it with Adam in mind! It was his favourite style and she knew she looked good in it.

A new wave of confidence washed over her. It was a long, long time since she'd felt as good as this. She wondered fleetingly how he was getting on with Barbara and could imagine the American girl tying herself in knots as she tried to worm her way out of this one!

She stood close to the mirror and her fingers shook as she fitted her earrings, the final touch. Ever since that magical kiss at the railway station, she'd been longing for this moment. She longed to recreate that magic, to bring back that feeling of complete joy and desire.

How much more wonderful it was going to be here, in the privacy of the flat, far away from prying eyes, far away from Barbara!

At that moment, the doorbell rang and she ran to answer it, running her hands nervously over her clothes to smooth them. She opened the door with a flourish, ready to stun Adam and saw, instead, Gerry standing there, grinning all over his face, a lovely bouquet of flowers in his arms!

Her disappointment was like a punch in the stomach and it took her a moment or two to collect herself. By that time, Gerry was striding purposefully into the flat.

'Adam sent me,' he announced cheerfully. 'I hope I'll do! There's been a bit of a crisis at home and he can't make it. He sends his apologies. I'll explain it all later! Hey, you look wonderful, Alison. That dress really does wonders for you.'

'Thank you,' she murmured, feeling crushed, automatically taking the flowers he proffered.

'I hear you've had a bit of a dust-up with Barbara?' He pulled a face. 'Never mind. What you need now is an evening out. It would be a crying shame to waste that gorgeous dress on these four walls. What do you say, Alison? I know a great little place, soft lights, sweet music and the most unbelievable food!'

'I don't know,' she wavered, unable to hide her disappointment. She'd planned on having an evening just as

Gerry described, but with Adam. Oh, why wasn't he here? How could he have let her down like this?

'Come on, honey,' Gerry coaxed gently.

She looked at his sincere, concerned face and somehow knew he understood much more than he was saying.

'OK. Why not?' she said in a subdued voice, shrugging her shoulders in a gesture of total resignation.

Gerry fetched her coat and draped it around her shoulders noticing, as he did, the gentle, creamy curve of her neck and the contrast between her pale skin and dark eyes. She was so lovely.

She was also very vulnerable and lonely, he reminded himself. He could see why Adam wanted so much to look after her. She evoked some very confusing and strong emotions.

'Thanks, Gerry,' Alison looked up at him and smiled, a warm, almost wistful little smile, unaware of his inner feelings.

His stomach seemed to be in knots.

She shouldn't be facing this all alone, he thought, she needs someone to lean on. She'd suffered so many disappointments already in her life, losing first Adam, then her baby, then Tim. She deserved some happiness now.

What she needs, he decided, is the right guy to lean on!

* * *

Adam was lying on a couch in the dark, nursing a splitting headache, when the doorbell rang and he groaned, wondering if it was Alison. He felt drained and empty. Alison was so dependent, so vulnerable, he didn't feel as if he could give her anything at the moment. The thought made him feel guilty.

The bell rang again and he staggered to his feet, stumbling through the darkness and switching on the lights as he made his way to the door.

'Pete!' He smiled in relief to find Jess Wheeler's husband on the doorstep. 'What brings you here?'

'I just wanted a word,' Pete said softly.

'Come on in.' Adam held the door open wide. 'I'll get you a drink.'

He'd met Pete before when he had walked Jess up to the house. He seemed a nice man, although rather quiet. He was stocky, with sandy hair and sad blue eyes which had a kind of haunted quality, Adam thought.

'I won't keep you long, Mr Simmons,' he said. 'I know how busy you are! I just wanted to say thank you for all you've done.'

Adam handed him a drink and shook his head. He felt unworthy of Pete's gratitude and said so. But Pete Wheeler thought differently.

'I'd never have believed people could be so kind. Barbara's been marvellous, a tower of strength, not just over this business with Nicola, but all the time.

'She been a real friend to us, Mr Simmons. You've got a wife in a million there. She really *cares* about other people!'

'If there's anything at all I can do,'

Adam said hoarsely, 'you just let me know. It won't be easy for you with Jess out of the country, and I'd like to do all I can to help.'

'That's good of you, Mr Simmons.' Pete grinned. 'But the older kids are good, you know. They all muck in and help.' He swallowed his drink and put the glass down. 'Like I said, I don't want to keep you. I just wanted to say thanks.'

'I just wish there was something more,' Adam said, feeling helpless.

'I know my girl's going to get better,' Pete said vehemently. 'I know she is. If only I could get a job . . . ' His eyes hardened. 'I hate to see my wife working her fingers to the bone because I can't provide. I've even had to rely on the charity of others to save my own child's life!

'I'm sorry!' Pete shrugged his shoulders. 'Jess says we should count our blessings. I suppose she's right.'

'It's not *your* fault, Pete,' Adam said thickly.

'That's what everyone tells me,' Pete replied, smiling ruefully, as he headed for the front door. 'I'll let you know if I hear anything, but I expect Barbara will be keeping in touch with you.'

Adam closed the door thoughtfully, and returned to the lounge, pulling the curtains shut. Pete was right about Barbara.

She cared, cared deeply!

In fact, he'd fallen in love with her because she cared so much about eveything — other people, animals, the environment, anything too weak, too sick or just plain unable to stand up for itself!

Barbara would always step in and help. She was seriously devoted to her causes and he was only beginning now to understand why. He'd never really bothered to listen to her arguments on behalf of the conservation society before, dismissing them as a load of cranks. He'd failed to see how important it was to her and, in doing that, he'd failed her.

And she did have a point! If people like her and himself, who had the means to get involved, didn't care about the environment, it wouldn't take long for it to be destroyed. And all in the name of progress!

Barbara was right to consider the future of their children. Yet men like Pete were desperate for work. He'd looked worried sick, browbeaten and worn out, as if he'd taken just about as many knocks as a man could bear.

Adam banged the table with his fist. It was high time he got off the fence and made a decision! He would go ahead with his project. People like Pete needed the jobs it would create. But, before he laid a single foundation stone, he would consult the conservationists!

They would be able to advise him on how best to proceed with the building project without harming too much of the area round about. There might be no need to disrupt the habitat of the wildlife completely.

He could almost visualise his buildings now, nestling in the countryside, unobtrusive, a stream running through the grounds, new wildlife habitats created if necessary.

He clenched his fists at his side. There had to be a way which would be of benefit to everyone and everything. He only hoped his decision hadn't been made too late to show Barbara that she'd been right.

* * *

Barbara held tightly to Jess's hand and looked reassuringly at her. In the next room, Nicola was undergoing a thorough examination by Dr Horrell himself. They had been waiting for some time, both saying very little.

'Did you call your parents?' Jess whispered, anxious to say something, longing to break the interminable silence.

Barbara nodded. 'I'm going to see them soon, once I'm sure you and

143

Nicola are settled. They only live a couple of hundred miles away.'

The door opened and the doctor breezed in. He was a big man with thick, bushy eyebrows and a broad smile. He pulled up a chair right in front of Jess and grasped both her hands in his. His manner was friendly and informal.

'Mrs Wheeler,' he began, his voice soft, his accent pleasant, 'we have one sick little girl in there, but I think I can help!'

Jess and Barbara let out their breath together, both unaware that they had been been holding it. The doctor smiled, looking from one white, worried face to the other.

'The treatment is slow and, unfortunately, expensive,' he went on. 'However, there is one bed still available in the unit and I'm willing to let Nicola have it.

'This afternoon, I intend to begin a series of tests which will determine exactly which course of treatment Nicola should receive. I'll be able to tell you more once the results are known. The main thing is, there's real hope.'

He gave Jess's hand a reassuring squeeze, stood up, gave the two women a warm smile, then hurried off down the corridor.

Jess, overwhelmed with relief, turning to hug Barbara, but saw, to her horror that Barbara was slipping slowly off her chair.

'Barbara!' she cried, jumping up and rushing to stop Barbara's head striking the floor. But the younger women was out cold, unable to respond and Jess frantically called for the help of a nurse.

Some time later, Barbara began to come round. She opened her eyes and looked startled at the unfamiliar surroundings. It took her a moment or two to remember where she was, then she realised she was lying on a bed in a consulting room.

'Hi, honey.' A nurse leaned over her, her face wreathed in smiles, her dark brown eyes shining. 'Feeling a little better now?'

'What happened?'

Barbara tried to sit up and the nurse helped her at once, putting a plump arm behind her back to support her. The nurse smoothed a strand of hair away from Barbara's face and studied her for a moment with motherly concern.

'You just fainted, honey,' she said. 'That's all!'

Barbara pressed her fingers into her forehead, confused. She didn't remember fainting. She never had before!

'Don't look so worried.' The nurse laughed and handed Barbara a glass of water. 'It doesn't happen very often, but, sometimes, ladies in your condition can't help themselves. It soon passes, along with the morning sickness.'

Barbara stared at her, open-mouthed. The nurse couldn't mean what she thought she meant!

'Don't say you hadn't realised!' The nurse laughed again. 'We'll run some tests, but I'm sure you'll find that I'm right. You're having a baby!'

6

Adam glanced quickly around the table, looking in turn at each of those seated. Everyone, without exception, was pleased with the meeting, and no-one more so than he was!

Just over a week ago, none of this had seemed possible but, now, it was as good as done.

'Well, ladies and gentlemen,' he said and, immediately, all eyes turned to look at him. 'If there are no more comments or suggestions, it looks as if it's all systems go! Thank you all for your co-operation. This should be an attractive and enviable site and, hopefully, a step in the right direction for future developments.'

'Hear, hear!' Bob, who headed the delegation from the conservation society, grinned. 'I think we all agree with that, Adam.'

147

'Good! Then I declare this meeting closed.'

As the others filed out, Adam went over to the projector which threw a detailed plan on to a large screen. He smiled. It had been hard work persuading everyone to scrap the original, agreed plans for the building and go for this, a completely new site, but he had done it!

Taking a last look around the boardroom, he switched off the projector and the lights and locked the door. Then, grabbing his briefcase, he hurried down to his car.

Now he could guarantee that job for Pete Wheeler, too, when they left school.

As he drove home, the roads were quiet and his mind drifted. It had been ten days since Barbara left for America with Nicola and Jess Wheeler. It felt like a life-time and, though she called every other day, he was missing her dreadfully.

Each night, without fail, he would

wake and run his hand across the empty half of the bed, wishing she was there, wishing she'd come home. At least the news of Nicola was good. They had started the treatment and, though Jess had warned it would take time, the results so far had been extremely encouraging.

Barbara had told Adam that both Nicola and Jess were bearing up well and taking it all in their stride. But she didn't mention a word about herself and had said nothing about coming home. He didn't want to pressure her, but he longed to see her again.

In the last few days, after meeting Barbara's friends, he'd realised that they weren't a bunch of 'green' cranks as he'd so readily dismissed them in the past. They were normal people, just like him, who had one thing in common — they cared.

It was just a pity that it had taken Barbara's walking out on him to make him see sense, too. In future, he would be more understanding. That's always assuming we have a future together, he thought grimly.

Bringing his car to a halt, he rushed indoors, hoping to hear the telephone, but the house was silent. As he buttered some bread and made himself a coffee, he looked accusingly at the phone. Why didn't she call?

An hour and a half later, he'd finished eating, read the day's paper and watched the television news. Yet there was still no word from America!

He was becoming more and more worried now. Barbara normally rang just before she had lunch. Now it would be about two o'clock in the afternoon in California. So where was she? Had she finally made her decision about the future? Did her future include him, or not?

He shook his head, desperately trying to convince himself that she had simply forgotten, or was unable, for some good reason, to phone just now.

★   ★   ★

Barbara was sitting in front of a dressing-table mirror, staring at her own reflection.

She felt as though she was glowing inside, despite her uncertainty about her marriage. It was being pregnant, of course. It had given her a wonderful, tranquil look.

She touched her flat stomach with her hand and shivered with delight. Safely in there was the baby she'd longed for — Adam's baby. Her smile turned to a frown. Would Adam share her joy? Should she even tell him about it, or had the baby come too late?

'Barbara!'

Her mother was calling her from downstairs. She shook herself from her reverie, got up and hurried out of the bedroom. At the bottom of the wide staircase, her mother, Nancy, waited.

'Where's Daddy?'

'He's gone to play golf. I asked him to,' Nancy said. 'I thought it was time I had my daughter to myself for a while.

Come on! Let's have our lunch in the garden.'

Barbara tensed. Surely her mother hadn't noticed anything wrong? Nothing in the older woman's eyes said so, but she could be pretty shrewd. Barbara had caught her watching her sometimes with a puzzled, concerned frown.

'You know, darling, you look even more gorgeous today,' Nancy said proudly. 'I've seen an improvement in you just over the past ten days. You must be happy, being pregnant!'

'Yes, of course I am.' Barbara stared down at her food, conscious of her mother's probing eyes.

'You're not still worrying about the little girl?' she persisted. 'I understood that she was making fine progress.'

'Oh, she is,' Barbara assured her quickly. 'The doctor is very hopeful she'll make a full recovery eventually.'

Nancy smiled. 'I'm glad to hear that, honey,' she said. Then, clasping her hands together, she went on, 'I must talk to you.'

'Is something wrong, Mother?' Barbara asked, concerned at the serious expression on her mother's face.

'I'm hoping you'll tell me,' Nancy said gently. 'I've noticed that something's wrong. You've been so quiet most of the time, withdrawn almost. Your father says I'm imagining things, but I think I know my own daughter well enough to know that you're desperately unhappy about something.'

Barbara shrugged. 'I'm just tired, you know, the travelling, worrying about Nicola and . . . '

'And? What about Adam?'

Nancy was met with the silence she had come to expect whenever Adam was mentioned and shook her head sorrowfully.

'You see! Every time I mention his name, you clam up completely. It's like getting blood from a stone, Barbara! If you don't clam up, then you change the subject, or suddenly remember something pressing you have to do. Darling, please, I'm worried about you. Surely you can confide in me?'

'You're right!' Barbara sighed deeply. 'Things between Adam and me have been strained for some weeks now.'

She broke off, took a moment or two to compose herself and realised that she was going to hurt her mother, who adored Adam and had heartily approved of their marriage. Now, she was going to disillusion her.

'I've stayed on here to take stock, to consider the future.'

'Go on.'

'It will probably sound silly,' Barbara said, clenching her fists, 'but our marriage is foundering and it all began when Alison came to stay.'

'Alison?'

Barbara turned to look at her mother. Taking a deep breath, she started to tell her everything, leaving nothing out, while her mother listened attentively. When she'd finished, she felt as if she'd just been relieved of a tremendous weight.

'So you see,' she concluded, 'things

were fine between us until he brought Alison home.'

Gently, Nancy drew Barbara into her arms, holding her tight, stroking her hair like she used to when Barbara was a child and was ill or frightened.

'Poor darling. Why on earth didn't you tell me all this sooner?' she said, mildly reproaching. 'I could have helped.'

'How?' Barbara was surprised.

She had expected her mother to be furious with Adam, not sitting there smiling as if what had happened was nothing.

'You young people nowadays!' She smiled. 'I think the only thing he's really guilty of is taking you for granted and failing to see how upset you were.'

'But, Alison . . . ?'

'Alison! You were happy before she arrived. You said so yourself!' Nancy pointed out firmly. 'You just have to ask yourself one very important question. Your whole future lies in the answer you give.'

'Just one question?' Barbara whispered.

'Oh, yes!' Nancy smiled and brushed Barbara's hair away from her face. 'That's all it takes, just one easy, little question and then you'll know what you have to do. Do you love Adam?'

'Of course I do!' Barbara said automatically.

Then her heart missed a beat. She'd answered her mother's question without thinking. She did still love Adam. So what was she going to do about it!

★ ★ ★

Gerry carried the coffees over to the table and grinned at Alison. He'd had more fun these past few days with her than at any other time since, well, since Jessica was alive.

He sat down on the couch and patted her hand in an affectionate gesture.

'Perhaps I should write a letter?' she suggested, her voice small. 'I know it's cowardly of me, Gerry,' she said, 'but I don't know what to say. I feel such a fool.'

'Adam doesn't think you're a fool, Alison, and, for what it's worth, neither do I,' Gerry said soberly. 'You've had a terrible time lately. It's no wonder you slipped off the rails a little. Anyway, once you're talking to Adam, it will be easy to say what you feel.'

'Will it?' she asked doubtfully.

He hugged her and she suddenly felt warmed right through. She would never have believed it possible that anyone could make her laugh so much again.

Gerry had barged into her life like a steam-roller, forcing her to look at herself. He'd practically bullied her into admitting that she was jealous of Barbara. Yet he'd also encouraged her to use her strength and experience to face a completely fresh start.

For ten years, she had unconsciously idolised Adam and, in the past few weeks, it had turned into an obsession. She felt ashamed now when she looked back and saw how she'd behaved.

Gerry's friendship, and uncompromising honesty, had helped her far more than kind words and sympathy!

'Thanks, Gerry,' she whispered.

'For what?'

'You know!' She smiled shyly and ran her fingers across his cheek. 'Just for being there.'

'Make the call,' he said encouragingly, then added with a grin, 'otherwise the poor guy will be in bed!'

When the telephone rang, it was so unexpected that Adam leaped from his chair and snatched it up. Barbara at last!

'Yes?' he said breathlessly. 'Adam Simmons here!'

'Adam, hello! It's Alison.'

His heart sank and he was surprised at how bitterly disappointed he was to hear Alison's voice. He looked at his watch irritably, hoping she wouldn't talk for too long and tie up the line.

'How are you, Alison?' he asked flatly. 'Everything all right?'

'Oh, really well, Adam!' she sounded

different somehow, more light-hearted, not as tense as before. 'I was calling to see how you were, actually, and to tell you I've moved to the boarding-house where Gerry stays.

'It's a smashing place, Adam, and Mrs Robinson is so nice. She mothers everyone. No wonder Gerry likes staying here so much!'

'Yes.' Adam sighed and looked again at his watch.

'Look, Adam, it's late. You must be tired, so I'll come straight to the point. I'm going home in the morning and I wanted to speak to you before I left. I wanted to apologise, Adam. You see, Gerry's been helping me get things into perspective and I now realise how much tension I caused between you and Barbara.

'I know it's no excuse, but I was so lonely, and seeing you two so happy made me realise what I'd missed. I guess I was jealous, Adam.'

Adam tried to speak, but didn't quite know what to say. For he, too, had been ashamed when he thought of how he'd treated Barbara. What could he say? Alison didn't sound self-pitying or miserable. She sounded positive and certain as if she'd regained control of her topsy-turvy life.

'Anyway,' Alison went on, 'I just called to say that I wish you both well. Perhaps we can all get together one of these days and be real friends? Oh, and Gerry's invited himself to stay with me in Norfolk for a few days before the new term starts. Should be a lot of fun.

'Look, I've already talked too much. Thanks for listening, Adam, and thanks just for everything. I mean it. You've been great.'

'That's what friends are for, Alison,' Adam said, subdued and feeling a little ashamed of his impatience. 'Just keep in touch, and take care of yourself.'

He paused for a moment after Alison had hung up, holding the phone against his chin, deep in thought.

So Gerry had been helping to bring about this change in Alison! But he shouldn't be surprised. Gerry was an expert in human nature and if he couldn't help, no-one could!

With a deep sigh, he put down the phone and went back to the kitchen to make coffee. He began to spoon coffee into his cup when the telephone rang and, without thinking, he just dropped the spoon and dived for the phone.

'Hi, Adam!'

He almost sank to his knees with relief.

'Barbara! I was getting worried. I thought you'd had an accident or something.'

'I'm sorry! I've been talking to my mother and I guess I forgot how late it was back in Britain.'

'How are things?' he said, hoping he sounded casual.

'Just about the same, Adam,' she murmured. 'Nicola's doing well.'

'Any idea when you'll be able to come home?' He dropped the question as lightly as he could.

'Actually, that's why I called,' she said casually.

For what seemed like ages, he held his breath, waiting for Barbara to go on. What decision had she come to?

'I'm flying home tomorrow,' she said, her words coming out in a rush, as if she'd been holding her breath, too! 'Jess will stay here, of course, and Mum and Dad have promised to keep an eye on her.

'My parents are both well and, as Nicola's making such good progress, there's no reason for me to stay on here any longer.'

'How about you?' he asked anxiously. 'Are you all right?'

'I'm OK,' she said softly. 'I've chatted everything through with my mother and I think I'm ready to talk to you now, Adam. But it isn't something we can do over the phone. There's too much to be said.'

'I'm just glad you're coming back,' Adam said softly, thankfully.

'It must be awfully late,' Barbara

went on. 'I'll ring off now and let you get some sleep.'

There was a brief silence and Adam impulsively yelled down the phone, 'I love you,' just before the line went dead.

In California, Barbara held the phone close to her heart. She'd had her fingers poised above the cut-off buttons when she'd heard his voice.

'I love you,' he'd said. Or had she imagined it? Was it too much to hope that he could still love her after all that had happened?

* * *

Gerry was standing in the airport lounge, but Barbara spotted him at once when he waved and shouted to her.

'Hi, Barbara!' He rushed over to her, his smile broader than she'd ever seen it. 'Wow, you look really great!'

'Where's Adam?' she said, biting her lip.

'Ah, I hope you don't mind me being here! I know I'm pretty poor substitute,' Gerry shrugged apologetically. 'But Adam's planning a big surprise for you.'

'So what's in this big surprise?' she said, as Gerry led her out to the car park. 'What's Adam up to?'

'You can torture me if you like,' Gerry said, closing his eyes. 'But I can't tell. He's sworn me to secrecy.'

Once they were in the car, Gerry turned to grin at her again.

'I'm glad you're back — Adam's been lost without you.' His face darkened. 'And I wanted the chance to talk to you anyway, about Alison.'

He saw Barbara go rigid at the mention of Alison's name and reached out to touch her hand reassuringly.

'She was staying with me, at Mrs Robinson's boarding-house.'

Barbara's eyes opened wide in surprise. This was the last thing she'd expected to hear! She had hoped, too, that she'd heard the last of Alison.

'She's gone home now, to get things

ready for the new term at school and I'm going to join her in a day or two, when I've finished my business here. The thing is, Barbara . . . '

He broke off, looking rather nervous.

'Well, she realises that she stirred things up between you and Adam and she's genuinely sorry. She's been confused, but she's starting to see things in a new light. She now knows she can't bring back the past and she's looking to the future.'

Barbara smiled and squeezed his hand. It would be a long time before she could forgive or trust Alison, but anything was possible.

'It's time we all made new starts I think, Gerry,' she said. 'I get the feeling you're quite fond of her.'

He smiled. 'Perhaps I'm not such a loner after all!'

After he'd dropped her off, Barbara stood and waved to Gerry as his car disappeared down the lane. Then she turned to look at the house. Just for a while, she hadn't been sure she'd ever come back here. She'd certainly never believed she'd be pregnant and feeling as hopeful as she did! But, this was no time for doubts. It was now or never.

Adam was in the hall, waiting for her. She could tell he was as nervous and unsure as she was. For a few seconds, they just stared at each other, then Adam said shakily, 'Welcome home, Barbara! It's so good to see you.'

He moved forward and hugged her tentatively, a little awkwardly, as if he were half afraid of rejection. She was trembling. He could feel it, and so was he.

He moved back, holding her hands, his eyes never leaving her face, as if he could still hardly believe that she was here.

'What's happened to you, Barbara?' he said. 'You've always been beautiful, but you look different, even more radiant, somehow.'

She reached up and smoothed his ruffled hair with her fingers.

'I feel fine, really well. But you look

tired, Adam. Have you been looking after yourself properly?'

'Never mind me!' he replied, relaxing a little. 'I feel better now you're back. But I'm forgetting about your surprise! Close your eyes and give me your hands. I'll lead you to it,' he said, guiding her into the lounge.

In the middle of the room, he'd set up Barbara's big easel and, on it, he'd pinned the plans for the new complex. He waited until he'd positioned her right in front of it, then released her.

'OK, you can look now!'

She blinked. It took a moment for her eyes to adjust.

'What's this?' She moved closer to the drawings. 'It looks like . . . Adam, it's your new place! But it's nothing like the original and it's on a different site, isn't it?'

She shook her head in wonder. In the artist's impression, the low buildings nestled unobtrusively in the country-side.

'We're going to plant some trees

here, here and here.' He pointed to various places. 'And we're also going to install a large pond, just here. We're building on the site of that disused factory.

'So you see, we won't be stealing any of the countryside. In fact, we'll be able to give a little back.'

'What about the original plans? You'd already bought the land.'

'I managed to convince the American directors that it would be an excellent public relations and publicity move to donate the land to the conservation society.'

She looked at him. His face was flushed, his eyes bright, like a child waiting for parental approval.

'Do you like it?' he asked nervously. 'I got together with Bob and the others at the conservation society to work on the plans. It's a joint effort. I've seen Pete Wheeler, too, and promised him a job in the near future. It's all coming to fruition, Barbara. What do you think?'

'It's beautiful, Adam,' she said at last.

'You've got it just right.'

He turned her round gently to look at him.

'I've compromised with the society,' he said at last. 'I want to compromise with you, too. I love you, Barbara. I don't want to lose you. I've been thinking hard about us and our future.

'I've missed you so much,' he said, reaching out to touch her face. 'It's been so lonely and empty here without you.'

They stood inches apart, both longing to break down the final barrier which stood between them.

'Oh, Adam!' Barbara cried. 'Come here!'

Adam needed no second bidding, taking her into his arms. They were laughing and crying all at once, their words stumbling out between reassuring kisses.

'I've been so stupid,' Barbara said. 'I was wrong not to trust you. I love you so much.'

'I never realised how much I needed

you until you'd gone. I can't live without you, believe me, Barbara.'

'We'll have to talk more,' Barbara pointed out. 'We shouldn't bottle things up.'

'Just listen to us.' Adam laughed. 'We sound so corny!'

For a long time, they held each other, revelling in the closeness they had both feared lost for ever.

'Adam,' Barbara whispered softly after a while, and he pulled away slightly so that he could see her face.

Her eyes were still moist with tears, but her mouth was turned up at the corners and her cheeks were rosy. 'I've got a surprise for you, too!'

★ ★ ★

It was a full year later. Barbara fed their son, Matthew, while Adam watched adoringly, his eyes full of love for the two of them.

'Well?' Barbara said, her eyes twinkling.

'Well what?' Adam said, coming out of his daydream.

'What did the postman bring?'

Adam looked down at the bundle of letters in his hand and began to flick through them. 'Circulars mostly. Hold on, though, what's this?'

He looked puzzled for a moment, then tore open the large, square envelope which was addressed in vaguely-familiar handwriting.

'Ah, it's from Alison!' he said, smiling. 'It's an invitation to a wedding!'

'Alison and Gerry?' Barbara sat the baby up and began to pat his back, her face wreathed in smiles. 'I can't say I'm surprised. They've never been out of each other's company for months. Besides, it'll be nice if Matthew's godparents are married!'

Adam laughed at that. 'What an incurable romantic you are!'

'I've got time to be, but you haven't! If you hang around much longer, you'll be late for work and in the way when Jess comes!'

171

Adam leaped up and dropped the rest of the mail on the table. He bent down and kissed first his son, then his wife. 'I'll see you later.'

'Don't be late tonight,' Barbara called after him.

'What?' He peered round the door. 'And miss my son and heir having his bath!' He blew them a kiss before hurrying out.

'Well, young man.' Barbara bounced Matthew on her knee. 'We'd better get you washed and dressed if we're going to the park with Jess and Nicola today.'

Unexpectedly her eyes filled with tears. But they were quickly banished as Matthew laughed up at her, proudly displaying one, solitary tooth.

She had never been happier than she was today.

THE END

OLD DESIRES

Liz Fielding

Joshua Kent infuriated Holly — he was arrogant, overbearing and convinced she was a good-for-nothing gold-digger! But even worse was his bombshell that her past was a complete fabrication. A new identity — and the inheritance which went with it — meant that Holly could embark on a fresh life for herself. But where did Joshua fit into the scheme of things? Was he just using the desire which flared between them to manipulate her? Only time would tell . . .

OUT OF THE BLUE

Chrissie Loveday

Bryher is tempted into a race on her motorbike one morning, with little idea of the chain of events that will follow. A new job leads to an unexpected meeting and a whole new career. Tristan seems to think an attractive female can oil the wheels of business. Never! She might fall for another biker, or a surfer perhaps . . . but an accountant? There's certainly no future here . . . or is there?